# ICE Conditions of Contract
# 5th and 6th editions
# compared

Thomas Telford, London

Published by Thomas Telford Ltd, Thomas Telford House, 1 Heron Quay, London E14 4JD

British Library Cataloguing in Publication Data
"The ICE Conditions of Contract" 5th and 6th compared.
346.41
ISBN 0 7277 16336 0

Printed and bound in the United Kingdom by Staples Printers Rochester Limited, Love Lane, Rochester, Kent.

# Preface

This publication provides an easy to use, clause-by-clause comparison of the changes between the 5th edition and the 6th edition of the ICE Conditions of Contract.

The 5th edition of the ICE Conditions of Contract has been in use as the standard contractual document for civil engineering works in a virtually unchanged form for 18 years. However, in 1988 the Conditions of Contract Standing Joint Committee decided that changes in industry practices required a thorough review of the whole document. The results of this review have now been published as the ICE Conditions of Contract 6th edition. It is the view of the CCSJC that the 6th edition does not introduce significant changes in the balance of responsibilities between the parties. However, a substantial proportion of the document has been rewritten to remove anomalies, improve clarity and, wherever possible, make the document more readable by the break-down of long clauses. Therefore users of the 5th edition will find the wording of the 6th edition unfamiliar even though the meaning of a particular clause may not have changed.

This comparative document presents the wording of the 5th edition opposite new wording from the 6th edition with changed clauses highlighted in colour. Explanatory notes are included giving details of significant changes. These are printed in colour under the relevant clauses. A descriptive list of general changes is given at the beginning of the book.

# Disclaimer

The information contained in this publication is intended for use as a general statement and guide only. Neither the Institution nor any committee of the Institution can accept any liability for any loss or damage which may be suffered by any person as a result of the use in any way of the information contained herein and any person using such information or drafting contracts, specifications or other documents based thereon must in all cases take appropriate professional advice on the matters referred to in this publication and are themselves solely responsible for ensuring that any wording taken from this document is consistent with and appropriate to the remainder of their material.

# General changes

A number of changes of a general nature have been made in the sixth edition of the ICE Conditions of Contract, most of which involve changes in the wording of a number of Clauses or sub-clauses. To avoid repetition throughout this commentary these changes are given below.

A. The general description "construct complete and maintain" has in nearly all cases been changed to "construct and complete" on the basis that the Works are complete only when all work of repair amendment reconstruction rectification and making good of defects has been completed. To avoid confusion, the term "maintenance" is not now being used.

B. In general the definitions previously included in Clauses throughout the Conditions have been included in Clause 1(1). However, in the case of the "Works Commencement Date" and the "Defects Correction Certificate" (Clauses 1(1)(q) and 1(1)(t)) the definitions, for convenience, refer to other Clauses in the Conditions.

C. The descriptive terms used in connection with the completion of a Contract have been changed for greater clarity as follows

- "Certification of Completion" (Clause 48) has been changed to "Certification of Substantial Completion" (Clause 1(1)(r))
- "Period of Maintenance" (Clause 49(1)) has been changed to "Defects Correction Period" (Clause 1(1)(s))
- "Maintenance Certificate" (Clause 61(1)) has been changed to "Defects Correction Certificate" (Clause 1(1)(t))

D. "Constructional Plant" has been changed to "Contractor's Equipment".

E. The definition of "Cost" (Clause 1(5)) clearly states that cost includes all on-costs but does not include any allowance for profit. In the Clauses that provide for the reimbursement of a Contractor's "extra cost" (Clauses 13(3), 14(8), 31(2), 40(1) and 42(3)) it is made clear that profit is to be added to such extra cost where the extra cost is in respect of additional permanent or temporary work but not where the extra cost relates only to inconvenience for the Contractor. For this reason the provision for adding profit to cost is not included in Clause 7(4).

**5th**

# TABLE OF CONTENTS

# CONTENTS OF ICE CONDITIONS OF CONTRACT

6<sup>th</sup>

5th



## LABOUR

# WORKMANSHIP AND MATERIALS

# COMMENCEMENT TIME AND DELAYS

# LIQUIDATED DAMAGES AND LIMITATION OF DAMAGES FOR DELAYED COMPLETION

# COMPLETION CERTIFICATE

# MAINTENANCE AND DEFECTS

## WORKMANSHIP AND MATERIALS

## COMMENCEMENT TIME AND DELAYS

## LIQUIDATED DAMAGES FOR DELAY

## CERTIFICATE OF SUBSTANTIAL COMPLETION

## OUTSTANDING WORK AND DEFECTS

## ALTERATIONS ADDITIONS AND OMISSIONS

## PROPERTY IN MATERIALS AND PLANT

## MEASUREMENT

## PROVISIONAL AND PRIME COST SUMS AND NOMINATED SUB-CONTRACTS

## ALTERATIONS ADDITIONS AND OMISSIONS

## PROPERTY IN MATERIALS AND CONTRACTOR'S EQUIPMENT

## MEASUREMENT

## PROVISIONAL AND PRIME COST SUMS AND NOMINATED SUB-CONTRACTS

# CERTIFICATES AND PAYMENT

# REMEDIES AND POWERS

# FRUSTRATION

# WAR CLAUSE

# SETTLEMENT OF DISPUTES

# APPLICATION TO SCOTLAND

# NOTICES

# CERTIFICATES AND PAYMENT

# REMEDIES AND POWERS

# FRUSTRATION

# WAR CLAUSE

# SETTLEMENT OF DISPUTES

# APPLICATION TO SCOTLAND

# NOTICES

**5**th

## TAX MATTERS

## SPECIAL CONDITIONS

6<sup>th</sup>

# Conditions of Contract

## DEFINITIONS AND INTERPRETATION

**Definitions.**    **1.**   (1)   In the Contract (as hereinafter defined) the following words and expressions shall have the meanings hereby assigned to them except where the context otherwise requires:—

    (a)   " Employer " means .................................................................................................
        of......................................................................................................................
        and includes the Employer's personal representatives or successors;

    (b)   " Contractor " means the person or persons firm or company whose tender has been accepted by the Employer and includes the Contractor's personal representatives successors and permitted assigns;

    (c)   "Engineer" means..........................................................................................
        or other Engineer appointed from time to time by the Employer and notified in writing to the Contractor to act as Engineer for the purposes of the Contract in place of the said...........................................................................................;

    (d)   " Engineer's Representative " means a person being the resident engineer or assistant of the Engineer or clerk of works appointed from time to time by the Employer or the Engineer and notified in writing to the Contractor by the Engineer to perform the functions set forth in Clause 2(1);

    (e)   " Contract " means the Conditions of Contract Specification Drawings Priced Bill of Quantities the Tender the written acceptance thereof and the Contract Agreement (if completed);

    (f)   " Specification " means the specification referred to in the Tender and any modification thereof or addition thereto as may from time to time be furnished or approved in writing by the Engineer;

    (g)   " Drawings " means the drawings referred to in the Specification and any modification of such drawings approved in writing by the Engineer and such other drawings as may from time to time be furnished or approved in writing by the Engineer;

    (h)   " Tender Total " means the total of the Priced Bill of Quantities at the date of acceptance of the Contractor's Tender for the Works;

14

# ICE Conditions of Contract

6<sup>th</sup>

## DEFINITIONS AND INTERPRETATION

**Definitions** **1** (1) In the Contract (as hereinafter defined) the following words and expressions shall have the meanings hereby assigned to them except where the context otherwise requires.

> (a) "Employer" means the person or persons firm company or other body named in the Appendix to the Form of Tender and includes the Employer's personal representatives successors and permitted assigns.

*The definition of "Employer" has been altered so that the name has to be entered in the Appendix to the Form of Tender.*

> (b) "Contractor" means the person or persons firm or company to whom the Contract has been awarded by the Employer and includes the Contractor's personal representatives successors and permitted assigns.

*The definition of "Contractor" has been altered to refer to the award of a Contract instead of to the acceptance of a tender.*

> (c) "Engineer" means the person firm or company appointed by the Employer to act as Engineer for the purposes of the Contract and named in the Appendix to the Form of Tender or such other person firm or company so appointed from time to time by the Employer and notified in writing as such to the Contractor.

*The definition of "Engineer" has been altered so that the name has to be entered in the Appendix to the Form of Tender.*

(d) "Engineer's Representative" means a person notified as such from time to time by the Engineer under Clause 2(3)(a).

(e) "Contract" means the Conditions of Contract Specification Drawings Bill of Quantities the Tender the written acceptance thereof and the Contract Agreement (if completed).

(f) "Specification" means the specification referred to in the Tender and any modification thereof or addition thereto as may from time to time be furnished or approved in writing by the Engineer.

(g) "Drawings" means the drawings referred to in the Specification and any modification of such drawings approved in writing by the Engineer and such other drawings as may from time to time be furnished or approved in writing by the Engineer.

(h) "Bill of Quantities" means the priced and completed Bill of Quantities.

(i) "Tender Total" means the total of the Bill of Quantities at the date of award of the Contract or in the absence of a Bill of Quantities the agreed estimated total value of the Works at that date.

(i) " Contract Price " means the sum to be ascertained and paid in accordance with the provisions hereinafter contained for the construction completion and maintenance of the Works in accordance with the Contract;

(j) " Permanent Works " means the permanent works to be constructed completed and maintained in accordance with the Contract;

(k) " Temporary Works " means all temporary works of every kind required in or about the construction completion and maintenance of the Works;

(l) " Works " means the Permanent Works together with the Temporary Works;

(m) " Section " means a part of the Works separately identified in the Appendix to the Form of Tender;

(n) " Site " means the lands and other places on under in or through which the Works are to be executed and any other lands or places provided by the Employer for the purposes of the Contract;

(o) " Constructional Plant " means all appliances or things of whatsoever nature required in or about the construction completion and maintenance of the Works but does not include materials or other things intended to form or forming part of the Permanent Works.

**Singular and Plural.**     (2) Words importing the singular also include the plural and *vice-versa* where the context requires.

(j) "Contract Price" means the sum to be ascertained and paid in accordance with the provisions hereinafter contained for the construction and completion of the Works in accordance with the Contract.

(k) "Prime Cost (PC) Item" means an item in the Contract which contains (either wholly or in part) a sum referred to as Prime Cost (PC) which will be used for the execution of work or the supply of goods materials or services for the Works.

(l) "Provisional Sum" means a sum included and so designated in the Contract as a specific contingency for the execution of work or the supply of goods materials or services which may be used in whole or in part or not at all at the direction and discretion of the Engineer.

(m) "Nominated Sub-contractor" means any merchant tradesman specialist or other person firm or company nominated in accordance with the Contract to be employed by the Contractor for the execution of work or supply of goods materials or services for which a Prime Cost has been inserted in the Contract or ordered by the Engineer to be employed by the Contractor to execute work or supply goods materials or services under a Provisional Sum.

(n) "Permanent Works" means the permanent works to be constructed and completed in accordance with the Contract.

(o) "Temporary Works" means all temporary works of every kind required in or about the construction and completion of the Works.

(p) "Works" means the Permanent Works together with the Temporary Works.

(q) "Works Commencement Date"—as defined in Clause 41(1).

(r) "Certificate of Substantial Completion" means a certificate issued under Clause 48(2)(a) 48(3) or 48(4).

(s) "Defects Correction Period" means that period stated in the Appendix to the Form of Tender calculated from the date on which the Contractor becomes entitled to a Certificate of Substantial Completion for the Works or any Section or part thereof.

(t) "Defects Correction Certificate"—as defined in Clause 61 (1).

(u) "Section" means a part of the Works separately identified in the Appendix to the Form of Tender.

(v) "Site" means the lands and other places on under in or through which the Works are to be executed and any other lands or places provided by the Employer for the purposes of the Contract together with such other places as may be designated in the Contract or subsequently agreed by the Engineer as forming part of the Site.

*The definition of "Site" has been extended to cover additional areas subsequently agreed by the Engineer as forming part of the Site.*

(w) "Contractors's Equipment" means all appliances or things of whatsoever nature required in or about the construction and completion of the Works but does not include materials or other things intended to form or forming part of the Permanent Works.

**Singular and plural**

(2) Words importing the singular also include the plural and vice-versa where the context requires.

**Headings and Marginal Notes.**

(3) The headings and marginal notes in the Conditions of Contract shall not be deemed to be part thereof or be taken into consideration in the interpretation or construction thereof or of the Contract.

**Clause References.**

(4) All references herein to clauses are references to clauses numbered in the Conditions of Contract and not to those in any other document forming part of the Contract.

**Cost.**

(5) The word " cost " when used in the Conditions of Contract shall be deemed to include overhead costs whether on or off the Site except where the contrary is expressly stated.

## ENGINEER'S REPRESENTATIVE

**Functions and Powers of Engineer's Representative.**

2. (1) The functions of the Engineer's Representative are to watch and supervise the construction completion and maintenance of the Works. He shall have no authority to relieve the Contractor of any of his duties or obligations under the Contract nor except as expressly provided hereunder to order any work involving delay or any extra payment by the Employer nor to make any variation of or in the Works.

**Headings and marginal notes**

(3) The headings and marginal notes in the Conditions of Contract shall not be deemed to be part thereof or be taken into consideration in the interpretation or construction thereof or of the Contract.

**Clause references**

(4) All references herein to clauses are references to clauses numbered in the Conditions of Contract and not to those in any other document forming part of the Contract.

**Cost**

(5) The word "cost" when used in the Conditions of Contract means all expenditure properly incurred or to be incurred whether on or off the Site including overhead finance and other charges properly allocatable thereto but does not include any allowance for profit.

**Communications in writing**

(6) Communications which under the Contract are required to be "in writing" may be hand-written typewritten or printed and sent by hand post telex cable or facsimile.

*New Clause.*

## ENGINEER AND ENGINEER'S REPRESENTATIVE

**Duties and authority of Engineer**

**2** (1) (a) The Engineer shall carry out the duties specified in or necessarily to be implied from the Contract.

(b) The Engineer may exercise the authority specified in or necessarily to be implied from the Contract. If the Engineer is required under the terms of his appointment by the Employer to obtain the specific approval of the Employer before exercising any such authority particulars of such requirements shall be those set out in the Appendix to the Form of Tender. Any requisite approval shall be deemed to have been given by the Employer for any such authority exercised by the Engineer.

(c) Except as expressly stated in the Contract the Engineer shall have no authority to amend the Terms and Conditions of the Contract nor to relieve the Contractor of any of his obligations under the Contract.

*New Clause.*

**Named individual**

(2) (a) Where the Engineer as defined in Clause 1 (1)(c) is not a single named Chartered Engineer the Engineer shall within 7 days of the award of the Contract and in any event before the Works Commencement Date notify to the Contractor in writing the name of the Chartered Engineer who will act on his behalf and assume the full responsibilities of the Engineer under the Contract.

(b) The Engineer shall thereafter in like manner notify the Contractor of any replacement of the named Chartered Engineer.

*New Clause requiring a single named Chartered Engineer to carry out the duties of the Engineer under the Contract.*

**Engineer's Representative**

(3) (a) The Engineer's Representative shall be responsible to the Engineer who shall notify his appointment to the Contractor in writing.

(b) The Engineer's Representative shall watch and supervise the construction and completion of the Works. He shall have no authority

**Appointment of Assistants.**

(2) The Engineer or the Engineer's Representative may appoint any number of persons to assist the Engineer's Representative in the exercise of his functions under sub-clause (1) of this Clause. He shall notify to the Contractor the names and functions of such persons. The said assistants shall have no power to issue any instructions to the Contractor save in so far as such instructions may be necessary to enable them to discharge their functions and to secure their acceptance of materials or workmanship as being in accordance with the Specification and Drawings and any instructions given by any of them for those purposes shall be deemed to have been given by the Engineer's Representative.

**Delegation by Engineer.**

(3) The Engineer may from time to time in writing authorise the Engineer's Representative or any other person responsible to the Engineer to act on behalf of the Engineer either generally in respect of the Contract or specifically in respect of particular Clauses of these Conditions of Contract and any act of any such person within the scope of his authority shall for the purposes of the contract constitute an act of the Engineer. Prior notice in writing of any such authorisation shall be given by the Engineer to the Contractor. Such authorisation shall continue in force until such time as the Engineer shall notify the Contractor in writing that the same is determined. Provided that such authorisation shall not be given in respect of any decision to be taken or certificate to be issued under Clauses 12(3) 44 48 60(3) 61 63 and 66.

**Reference to Engineer or Engineer's Representative.**

(4) If the Contractor shall be dissatisfied by reason of any instruction of any assistant of the Engineer's Representative duly appointed under sub-clause (2) of this Clause he shall be entitled to refer the matter to the Engineer's Representative who shall thereupon confirm reverse or vary such instruction. Similarly if the Contractor shall be dissatisfied by reason of any act of the Engineer's Representative or other person duly authorised by the Engineer under sub-clause (3) of this Clause he shall be entitled to refer the matter to the Engineer for his decision.

(i) to relieve the Contractor of any of his duties or obligations under the Contract

nor except as expressly provided hereunder

(ii) to order any work involving delay or any extra payment by the Employer or

(iii) to make any variation of or in the Works.

*New Clause concerning the appointment of the Engineer's Representative but taken substantially from previous Clauses 1(1)(d) and 2(1).*

**Delegation by Engineer**

(4)  The Engineer may from time to time delegate to the Engineer's Representative or any other person responsible to the Engineer any of the duties and authorities vested in the Engineer and he may at any time revoke such delegation. Any such delegation

(a)  shall be in writing and shall not take effect until such time as a copy thereof has been delivered to the Contractor or his agent appointed under Clause 15(2)

(b)  shall continue in force until such time as the Engineer shall notify the Contractor in writing that the same has been revoked

(c)  shall not be given in respect of any decision to be taken or certificate to be issued under Clauses 12(6) 44 46(3) 48 60(4) 61 63 or 66.

**Assistants**

(5)  (a)  The Engineer or the Engineer's Representative may appoint any number of persons to assist the Engineer's Representative in the carrying out of his duties under sub-clause (3)(b) or (4) of this Clause. He shall notify to the Contractor the names duties and scope of authority of such persons.

(b)  Such assistants shall have no authority to issue any instructions to the Contractor save insofar as such instructions may be necessary to enable them to carry out their duties and to secure their acceptance of materials and workmanship as being in accordance with the Contract. Any instructions given by an assistant for these purposes shall where appropriate be in writing and be deemed to have been given by the Engineer's Representative.

(c)  If the Contractor is dissatisfied by reason of any instruction of any assistant of the Engineer's Representative appointed under sub-clause (5)(a) of this Clause he shall be entitled to refer the matter to the Engineer's Representative who shall thereupon confirm reverse or vary such instruction.

**Instructions**

(6)  (a)  Instructions given by the Engineer or by the Engineer's Representative exercising delegated duties and authorities under sub-clause (4) of this Clause shall be in writing. Provided that if for any reason it is considered necessary to give any such instruction orally the Contractor shall comply with such instruction.

(b)  Any such oral instruction shall be confirmed in writing by the Engineer or the Engineer's Representative as soon as is possible under the circumstances. Provided that if the Contractor shall confirm in writing any such oral instruction and such confirmation is not contradicted in writing by the Engineer or the Engineer's Representative forthwith it shall be deemed to be an instruction in writing by the Engineer.

## ASSIGNMENT AND SUB-LETTING

**Assignment.**      3.     The Contractor shall not assign the Contract or any part thereof or any benefit or interest therein or thereunder without the written consent of the Employer.

**Sub-Letting.**      4.     The Contractor shall not sub-let the whole of the Works. Except where otherwise provided by the Contract the Contractor shall not sub-let any part of the Works without the written consent of the Engineer and such consent if given shall not relieve the Contractor from any liability or obligation under the Contract and he shall be responsible for the acts defaults and neglects of any sub-contractor his agents servants or workmen as fully as if they were the acts defaults or neglects of the Contractor his agents servants or workmen. Provided always that the provision of labour on a piece-work basis shall not be deemed to be a sub-letting under this Clause.

(c)   Upon the written request of the Contractor the Engineer or the Engineer's Representative exercising delegated duties or authorities under sub-clause (4) of this Clause shall specify in writing under which of his duties and authorities any instruction is given.

*New sub-clauses: (a) requiring instructions to be in writing; (b) regarding the confirmation of verbal instructions; (c) requiring, upon request, the identification of the authority for any instruction. Taken substantially from previous Clause 51(2) lines 2-7.*

**Reference on dissatisfaction**

(7)   If the Contractor is dissatisfied by reason of any act or instruction of the Engineer's Representative he shall be entitled to refer the matter to the Engineer for his decision.

**Impartiality**

(8)   The Engineer shall except in connection with matters requiring the specific approval of the Employer under sub- clause (1)(b) of this Clause act impartially within the terms of the Contract having regard to all the circumstances.

*New Clause requiring the Engineer to act impartially except in specific instances where he has to obtain the approval of the Employer. Such a requirement has to be clearly set out in the Appendix to the Form of Tender.*

## ASSIGNMENT AND SUB-CONTRACTING

**Assignment**

**3**   Neither the Employer nor the Contractor shall assign the Contract or any part thereof or any benefit or interest therein or thereunder without the prior written consent of the other party which consent shall not unreasonably be withheld.

*Clause revised to give the Contractor equal protection against assignment of the Contract by the Employer.*

**Sub-contracting**

**4**   (1)   The Contractor shall not sub-contract the whole of the Works without the prior written consent of the Employer.

(2)   Except where otherwise provided the Contractor may sub-contract any part of the Works or their design. The extent of the work to be sub-contracted and the name and address of the sub-contractor must be notified in writing to the Engineer prior to the sub-contractor's entry on to the Site or in the case of design on appointment.

(3)   The employment of labour-only sub-contractors does not require notification to the Engineer under sub-clause(2) of this Clause.

(4)   The Contractor shall be and remain liable under the Contract for all work sub-contracted under this Clause and for acts defaults or neglects of any sub-contractor his agents servants or workpeople.

(5)   The Engineer shall be at liberty after due warning in writing to require the Contractor to remove from the Works any sub-contractor who mis-conducts himself or is incompetent or negligent in the performance of his duties or fails to conform with any particular provisions with regard to safety which may be set out in the Contract or persists in any conduct which is prejudicial to safety or health and such sub-contractor shall not be again employed upon the Works without the permission of the Engineer.

## CONTRACT DOCUMENTS

**Documents Mutually Explanatory.**

5.    The several documents forming the Contract are to be taken as mutually explanatory of one another and in case of ambiguities or discrepancies the same shall be explained and adjusted by the Engineer who shall thereupon issue to the Contractor appropriate instructions in writing which shall be regarded as instructions issued in accordance with Clause 13.

**Supply of Documents.**

6.    Upon acceptance of the Tender 2 copies of the drawings referred to in the Specification and of the Conditions of Contract the Specification and (unpriced) Bill of Quantities shall be furnished to the Contractor free of charge.   Copyright of the Drawings and Specification and of the Bill of Quantities (except the pricing thereof) shall remain in the Engineer but the Contractor may obtain or make at his own expense any further copies required by him.   At the completion of the Contract the Contractor shall return to the Engineer all Drawings and the Specification whether provided by the Engineer or obtained or made by the Contractor.

*This Clause has been revised in line with current practice recognizing that sub-contractors and the self-employed now constitute the major proportion of the labour force in the construction industry. Sub-contracting the whole of the Works requires the Employer's consent; sub-contracting a part of the Works requires prior notification to the Engineer. Employment of labour-only sub-contractors (previously referred to as labour employed on a piece-work basis) does not require prior notification. The Contractor is still fully responsible for all sub-contracted work (Clause 4(4)) and the Engineer has the specific right "after due warning in writing" to require the Contractor to remove from the Works any sub-contractor who misconducts himself (Clause 4(5)). This is additional to the powers given to the Engineer under Clause 16 to require the removal from the Works of any employee of a sub-contractor who misconducts himself.*

## CONTRACT DOCUMENTS

**Documents mutually explanatory**

**5** The several documents forming the Contract are to be taken as mutually explanatory of one another and in case of ambiguities or discrepancies the same shall be explained and adjusted by the Engineer who shall thereupon issue to the Contractor appropriate instructions in writing which shall be regarded as instructions issued in accordance with Clause 13.

**Supply of documents**

**6** (1) Upon award of the Contract the following shall be furnished to the Contractor free of charge

(a) four copies of the Conditions of Contract Specification and (unpriced) bill of quantities and

(b) the number and type of copies as entered in the Appendix to the Form of Tender of all Drawings listed in the Specification.

*The Contractor is now to be supplied with four copies of the Contract documents and the number and type of copies of the Drawings as stated in the Appendix to the Form of Tender.*

(2) Upon approval by the Engineer in accordance with Clause 7(6) the Contractor shall supply to the Engineer four copies of all Drawings Specifications and other documents submitted by the Contractor. In addition the Contractor shall supply at the Employer's expense such further copies of such Drawings Specifications and other documents as the Engineer may request in writing for his use.

*This Clause has been included to cover when appropriate the supply by the Contractor of copies of drawings, specifications or other documents to the Engineer.*

(3) Copyright of all Drawings Specifications and the Bill of Quantities (except the pricing thereof) supplied by the Employer or the Engineer shall not pass to the Contractor but the Contractor may obtain or make at his own expense any further copies required by him for the purposes of the Contract. Similarly copyright of all documents supplied by the Contractor under Clause 7(6) shall remain in the Contractor but the Employer and the Engineer shall have full power to reproduce and use the same for the purpose of completing operating maintaining and adjusting the Works.

*This Clause covers the copyright of all documents supplied by either of the parties to the Contract.*

**Further Drawings and Instructions.**

7. (1) The Engineer shall have full power and authority to supply and shall supply to the Contractor from time to time during the progress of the Works such modified or further drawings and instructions as shall in the Engineer's opinion be necessary for the purpose of the proper and adequate construction completion and maintenance of the Works and the Contractor shall carry out and be bound by the same.

**Notice by Contractor.**

(2) The Contractor shall give adequate notice in writing to the Engineer of any further drawing or specification that the Contractor may require for the execution of the Works or otherwise under the Contract.

**Delay in Issue.**

(3) If by reason of any failure or inability of the Engineer to issue at a time reasonable in all the circumstances drawings or instructions requested by the Contractor and considered necessary by the Engineer in accordance with sub-clause (1) of this Clause the Contractor suffers delay or incurs cost then the Engineer shall take such delay into account in determining any extension of time to which the Contractor is entitled under Clause 44 and the Contractor shall subject to Clause 52(4) be paid in accordance with Clause 60 the amount of such cost as may be reasonable. If such drawings or instructions require any variation to any part of the Works the same shall be deemed to have been issued pursuant to Clause 51.

**One Copy of Documents to be kept on Site.**

(4) One copy of the Drawings and Specification furnished to the Contractor as aforesaid shall be kept by the Contractor on the Site and the same shall at all reasonable times be available for inspection and use by the Engineer and the Engineer's Representative and by any other person authorised by the Engineer in writing.

**Further Drawings Specifications and instructions**

**7** (1)  The Engineer shall from time to time during the progress of the Works supply to the Contractor such modified or further Drawings Specifications and instructions as shall in the Engineer's opinion be necessary for the purpose of the proper and adequate construction and completion of the Works and the Contractor shall carry out and be bound by the same.

If such Drawings Specifications or instructions require any variation to any part of the works the same shall be deemed to have been issued pursuant to Clause 51.

**Contractor to provide further documents**

(2)  Where sub-clause (6) of this Clause applies the Engineer may require the Contractor to supply such further documents as shall in the Engineer's opinion be necessary for the purpose of the proper and adequate construction completion and maintenance of the Works and when approved by the Engineer the Contractor shall carry out and be bound by the same.

*New Clause to cover the supply of documents by the Contractor when any part of the Permanent Works is being designed by the Contractor.*

**Notice by Contractor**

(3)  The Contractor shall give adequate notice in writing to the Engineer of any further Drawing or Specification that the Contractor may require for the construction and completion of the Works or otherwise under the Contract.

**Delay in issue**

(4)  (a)  If by reason of any failure or inability of the Engineer to issue at a time reasonable in all the circumstances Drawings Specifications or instructions requested by the Contractor and considered necessary by the Engineer in accordance with sub-clause (1) of this Clause the Contractor suffers delay or incurs cost then the Engineer shall take such delay into account in determining any extension of time to which the Contractor is entitled under Clause 44 and the Contractor shall subject to Clause 52(4) be paid in accordance with Clause 60 the amount of such cost as may be reasonable.

(b)  If the failure of the Engineer to issue any Drawing Specification or instruction is caused in whole or in part by the failure of the Contractor after due notice in writing to submit drawings specifications or other documents which he is required to submit under the Contract the Engineer shall take into account such failure by the Contractor in taking any action under sub-clause (4)(a) of this Clause.

*New sub-clause to cover the effect of late provision of documentation by the Contractor.*

**One copy of documents to be kept on Site**

(5)  One copy of the Drawings and Specification furnished to the Contractor as aforesaid and of all Drawings Specifications and other documents required to be provided by the Contractor under sub-clause (6) of this Clause shall at all reasonable times be available on the Site for inspection and use by the Engineer and the Engineer's Representative and by any other person authorized by the Engineer in writing.

**Permanent Works designed by Contractor**

(6)  Where the Contract expressly provides that part of the Permanent Works shall be designed by the Contractor he shall submit to the Engineer for approval

(a)  such drawings specifications calculations and other information as shall be necessary to satisfy the Engineer as to the suitability and adequacy of the design and

27

## GENERAL OBLIGATIONS

**Contractor's General Responsibilities.**

**8.** (1) The Contractor shall subject to the provisions of the Contract construct complete and maintain the Works and provide all labour materials Constructional Plant Temporary Works transport to and from and in or about the Site and everything whether of a temporary or permanent nature required in and for such construction completion and maintenance so far as the necessity for providing the same is specified in or reasonably to be inferred from the Contract.

**Contractor Responsible for Safety of Site Operations.**

(2) The Contractor shall take full responsibility for the adequacy stability and safety of all site operations and methods of construction provided that the Contractor shall not be responsible for the design or specification of the Permanent Works (except as may be expressly provided in the Contract) or of any Temporary Works designed by the Engineer.

**Contract Agreement.**

**9.** The Contractor shall when called upon so to do enter into and execute a Contract Agreement (to be prepared at the cost of the Employer) in the form annexed.

**Sureties.**

**10.** If the Tender shall contain an undertaking by the Contractor to provide when required 2 good and sufficient sureties or to obtain the guarantee of an Insurance Company or Bank to be jointly and severally bound with the Contractor in a sum not exceeding 10 per cent of the Tender Total for the due performance of the Contract under the terms of a Bond the said sureties Insurance Company or Bank and the terms of the said Bond shall be such as shall be approved by the Employer and the provision of such sureties or the obtaining of such guarantee and the cost of the Bond to be so entered into shall be at the expense in all respects of the Contractor unless the Contract otherwise provides. Provided always that if the form of Bond approved by the Employer shall

(b) operation and maintenance manuals together with as completed drawings of that part of the Permanent Works in sufficient detail to enable the Employer to operate maintain dismantle reassemble and adjust the Permanent Works incorporating that design. No certificate under Clause 48 covering any part of the Permanent Works designed by the Contractor shall be issued until manuals and drawings in such detail have been submitted to and approved by the Engineer.

*This is a new Clause to cover Permanent Works design by the Contractor and deals with the supply by the Contractor of drawings, specifications, calculations, etc., and of operation and maintenance manuals.*

**Responsibility unaffected by approval**

(7)   Approval by the Engineer in accordance with sub-clause (6) of this Clause shall not relieve the Contractor of any of his responsibilities under the Contract. The Engineer shall be responsible for the integration and co-ordination of the Contractor's design with the rest of the Works.

*New Clause making the Engineer responsible for the integration and co-ordination of any Contractor-designed work with the rest of the Works.*

## GENERAL OBLIGATIONS

**Contractor's general responsibilities**

8   (1)   The Contractor shall subject to the provisions of the Contract

(a)   construct and complete the Works and

(b)   provide all labour materials Contractor's Equipment Temporary Works transport to and from and in or about the Site and everything whether of a temporary or permanent nature required in and for such construction and completion so far as the necessity for providing the same is specified in or reasonably to be inferred from the Contract.

**Design responsibility**

(2)   The Contractor shall not be responsible for the design or specification of the Permanent Works or any part thereof (except as may be expressly provided in the Contract) or of any Temporary Works designed by the Engineer. The Contractor shall exercise all reasonable skill care and diligence in designing any part of the Permanent Works for which he is responsible.

*Substantially as the second half of previous Clause 8(2) but the Contractor's design liability is limited to the use of reasonable skill care and diligence.*

**Contractor responsible for safety of site operations**

(3)   The Contractor shall take full responsibility for the adequacy stability and safety of all site operations and methods of construction.

**Contract Agreement**

9   The Contractor shall if called upon so to do enter into and execute a Contract Agreement to be prepared at the cost of the Employer in the form annexed to these Conditions.

**Performance security**

10   (1)   If the Contract requires the Contractor to provide security for the proper performance of the Contract he shall obtain and provide to the Employer such security in a sum not exceeding 10% of the Tender Total within 28 days of the award of the Contract. The security shall be provided by a body approved by the Employer and be in the Form of Bond annexed to these Conditions. The Contractor shall pay the cost of such security unless the Contract provides otherwise.

contain provisions for the determination by an arbitrator of any dispute or difference concerning the relevant date for the discharge of the Sureties'/Surety's obligations under the said Bond:—

   (a) the Employer shall be deemed to be a party to the said Bond for the purpose of doing all things necessary to carry such provisions into effect;

   (b) any agreement decision award or other determination touching or concerning the relevant date for the discharge of the Sureties'/Surety's obligations under the said Bond shall be wholly without prejudice to the resolution or determination of any dispute or difference between the Employer and the Contractor pursuant to the provisions of Clause 66.

**Inspection of Site.**

**11.** (1) The Contractor shall be deemed to have inspected and examined the Site and its surroundings and to have satisfied himself before submitting his tender as to the nature of the ground and sub-soil (so far as is practicable and having taken into account any information in connection therewith which may have been provided by or on behalf of the Employer) the form and nature of the Site the extent and nature of the work and materials necessary for the completion of the Works the means of communication with and access to the Site the accommodation he may require and in general to have obtained for himself all necessary information (subject as above-mentioned) as to risks contingencies and all other circumstances influencing or affecting his tender.

**Sufficiency of Tender.**

(2) The Contractor shall be deemed to have satisfied himself before submitting his tender as to the correctness and sufficiency of the rates and prices stated by him in the Priced Bill of Quantities which shall (except in so far as it is otherwise provided in the Contract) cover all his obligations under the Contract.

**Adverse Physical Conditions and Artificial Obstructions.**

**12.** (1) If during the execution of the Works the Contractor shall encounter physical conditions (other than weather conditions or conditions due to weather conditions) or artificial obstructions which conditions or obstructions he considers could not reasonably have been foreseen by an experienced contractor and the Contractor is of opinion that additional cost will be incurred which would not have been incurred if the physical conditions or artificial obstructions had not been encountered he shall if he intends to make any claim for additional payment give notice to the Engineer pursuant to Clause 52(4) and shall specify in such notice the physical conditions and/or

**Arbitration upon security**

(2)   For the purposes of the arbitration provisions in such security

(a)   the Employer shall be deemed a party to the said security for the purpose of doing everything necessary to give effect to such provisions and

(b)   any agreement decision award or other determination touching or concerning the relevant date for the discharge of such security shall be wholly without prejudice to the resolution or determination of any dispute or difference between the Employer and the Contractor under Clause 66.

**Provision and interpretation of information**

**11**   (1)   The Employer shall be deemed to have made available to the Contractor before the submission of the Tender all information on the nature of the ground and sub-soil including hydrological conditions obtained by or on behalf of the Employer from investigations undertaken relevant to the Works.

The Contractor shall be responsible for the interpretation of all such information for the purposes of constructing the Works and for any design which is the Contractor's responsibility under the Contract.

*New Clause under which the Employer is deemed to have made available to tenderers all existing relevant ground investigation data. The Contractor is made responsible for the interpretation of the information so provided for the purposes of constructing the Works and for any design for which the Contractor is responsible.*

**Inspection of Site**

(2)   The Contractor shall be deemed to have inspected and examined the Site and its surroundings and information available in connection therewith and to have satisfied himself so far as is practicable and reasonable before submitting his Tender as to

(a)   the form and nature thereof including the ground and sub-soil

(b)   the extent and nature of work and materials necessary for constructing and completing the Works and

(c)   the means of communication with and access to the Site and the accommodation he may require

and in general to have obtained for himself all necessary information as to risks contingencies and all other circumstances which may influence or affect his Tender.

**Basis and sufficiency of Tender**

(3)   The Contractor shall be deemed to have

(a)   based his Tender on the information made available by the Employer and on his own inspection and examination all as aforementioned and

*New sub-clause.*

(b)   satisfied himself before submitting his Tender as to the correctness and sufficiency of the rates and prices stated by him in the Bill of Quantities which shall (unless otherwise provided in the Contract) cover all his obligations under the Contract.

**Adverse physical conditions and artifical obstructions**

**12**   (1)   If during the execution of the Works the Contractor shall encounter physical conditions (other than weather conditions or conditions due to weather conditions) or artificial obstructions which conditions or obstructions could not in his opinion reasonably have been foreseen by an experienced contractor the Contractor shall as early as practicable give written notice thereof to the Engineer.

31

artificial obstructions encountered and with the notice if practicable or as soon as possible thereafter give details of the anticipated effects thereof the measures he is taking or is proposing to take and the extent of the anticipated delay in or interference with the execution of the Works.

**Measures to be Taken.**

(2)   Following receipt of a notice under sub-clause (1) of this Clause the Engineer may if he thinks fit *inter alia:*—

    (a)   require the Contractor to provide an estimate of the cost of the measures he is taking or is proposing to take;

    (b)   approve in writing such measures with or without modification;

    (c)   give written instructions as to how the physical conditions or artificial obstructions are to be dealt with;

    (d)   order a suspension under Clause 40 or a variation under Clause 51.

**Delay and Extra Cost.**

(3)   To the extent that the Engineer shall decide that the whole or some part of the said physical conditions or artificial obstructions could not reasonably have been foreseen by an experienced contractor the Engineer shall take any delay suffered by the Contractor as a result of such conditions or obstructions into account in determining any extension of time to which the Contractor is entitled under Clause 44 and the Contractor shall subject to Clause 52(4) (notwithstanding that the Engineer may not have given any instructions or orders pursuant to sub-clause (2) of this Clause) be paid in accordance with Clause 60 such sum as represents the reasonable cost of carrying out any additional work done and additional Constructional Plant used which would not have been done or used had such conditions or obstructions or such part thereof as the case may be not been encountered together with a reasonable percentage addition thereto in respect of profit and the reasonable costs incurred by the Contractor by reason of any unavoidable delay or disruption of working suffered as a consequence of encountering the said conditions or obstructions or such part thereof.

**Conditions Reasonably Foreseeable.**

(4)   If the Engineer shall decide that the physical conditions or artificial obstructions could in whole or in part have been reasonably foreseen by an experienced contractor he shall so inform the Contractor in writing as soon as he shall have reached that decision but the value of any variation previously ordered by him pursuant to sub-clause (2)(d) of this Clause shall be ascertained in accordance with Clause 52 and included in the Contract Price.

**Intention to claim**

(2)  If in addition the Contractor intends to make any claim for additional payment or extension of time arising from such condition or obstruction he shall at the same time or as soon thereafter as may be reasonable inform the Engineer in writing pursuant to Clause 52(4) and/ or Clause 44(1) as may be appropriate specifying the condition or obstruction to which the claim relates.

**Measures being taken**

(3)  When giving notification in accordance with sub-clauses (1) and (2) of this Clause or as soon as practicable thereafter the Contractor shall give details of any anticipated effects of the condition or obstruction the measures he has taken is taking or is proposing to take their estimated cost and the extent of the anticipated delay in or interference with the execution of the Works.

*The previous Clause 12(1) has been split into three separate Clauses. Clause 12(1) now calls for the earliest possible written notification to the Engineer of a Clause 12 situation. Clause 12(2) requires separate (or simultaneous) notification of the Contractor's intention to claim additional payment or extension of time. Clause 12(3) requires the Contractor, when giving notification under either of the previous two clauses (or as soon as possible thereafter), to give details of the anticipated effects, the measures he has taken or is proposing to take and their estimated cost and the possible delay or interference with the execution of the Works.*

**Action by Engineer**

(4)  Following receipt of any notification under sub-clauses (1) (2) or (3) of this Clause the Engineer may if he thinks fit inter alia

(a)  require the Contractor to investigate and report upon the practicality cost and timing of alternative measures which may be available

*New sub-clause.*

(b)  give written consent to measures notified under sub-clause (3) of this Clause with or without modification

(c)  give written instructions as to how the physical conditions or artificial obstructions are to be dealt with

(d)  order a suspension under Clause 40 or a variation under Clause 51.

**Conditions reasonably foreseeable**

(5)  If the Engineer shall decide that the physical conditions or artificial obstructions could in whole or in part have been reasonably foreseen by an experienced contractor he shall so inform the Contractor in writing as soon as he shall have reached that decision but the value of any variation previously ordered by him pursuant to sub-clause (4)(d) of this Clause shall be ascertained in accordance with Clause 52 and included in the Contract Price.

**Delay and extra cost**

(6)  Where an extension of time or additional payment is claimed pursuant to sub-clause (2) of this Clause the Engineer shall if in his opinion such conditions or obstructions could not reasonably have been foreseen by an experienced contractor determine the amount of any costs which may reasonably have been incurred by the Contractor by reason of such conditions or obstructions together with a reasonable percentage addition thereto in respect of profit and any extension of time to which the Contractor may be entitled and shall notify the Contractor accordingly with a copy to the Employer.

**Work to be to Satisfaction of Engineer.**

**13.** (1) Save in so far as it is legally or physically impossible the Contractor shall construct complete and maintain the Works in strict accordance with the Contract to the satisfaction of the Engineer and shall comply with and adhere strictly to the Engineer's instructions and directions on any matter connected therewith (whether mentioned in the Contract or not). The Contractor shall take instructions and directions only from the Engineer or (subject to the limitations referred to in Clause 2) from the Engineer's Representative.

**Mode and Manner of Construction.**

(2) The whole of the materials plant and labour to be provided by the Contractor under Clause 8 and the mode manner and speed of construction and maintenance of the Works are to be of a kind and conducted in a manner approved of by the Engineer.

**Delay and Extra Cost.**

(3) If in pursuance of Clause 5 or sub-clause (1) of this Clause the Engineer shall issue instructions or directions which involve the Contractor in delay or disrupt his arrangements or methods of construction so as to cause him to incur cost beyond that reasonably to have been foreseen by an experienced contractor at the time of tender then the Engineer shall take such delay into account in determining any extension of time to which the Contractor is entitled under Clause 44 and the Contractor shall subject to Clause 52(4) be paid in accordance with Clause 60 the amount of such cost as may be reasonable. If such instructions or directions require any variation to any part of the Works the same shall be deemed to have been given pursuant to Clause 51.

**Programme to be Furnished.**

**14.** (1) Within 21 days after the acceptance of his Tender the Contractor shall submit to the Engineer for his approval a programme showing the order of procedure in which he proposes to carry out the Works and thereafter shall furnish such further details and information as the Engineer may reasonably require in regard thereto. The Contractor shall at the same time also provide in writing for the information of the Engineer a general description of the arrangements and methods of construction which the Contractor proposes to adopt for the carrying out of the Works.

**Work to be to satisfaction of Engineer**

**13** (1) Save insofar as it is legally or physically impossible the Contractor shall construct and complete the Works in strict accordance with the Contract to the satisfaction of the Engineer and shall comply with and adhere strictly to the Engineer's instructions on any matter connected therewith (whether mentioned in the Contract or not). The Contractor shall take instructions only from the Engineer or (subject to the limitations referred to in Clause 2) from the Engineer's Representative.

**Mode and manner of construction**

(2) The whole of the materials plant and labour to be provided by the Contractor under Clause 8 and the mode manner and speed of construction of the Works are to be of a kind and conducted in a manner acceptable to the Engineer.

**Delay and extra cost**

(3) If in pursuance of Clause 5 or sub-clause (1) of this Clause the Engineer shall issue instructions which involve the Contractor in delay or disrupt his arrangements or methods of construction so as to cause him to incur cost beyond that reasonably to have been foreseen by an experienced contractor at the time of tender then the Engineer shall take such delay into account in determining any extension of time to which the Contractor is entitled under Clause 44 and the Contractor shall subject to Clause 52(4) be paid in accordance with Clause 60 the amount of such cost as may be reasonable except to the extent that such delay and extra cost result from the Contractor's default. Profit shall be added thereto in respect of any additional permanent or temporary work. If such instructions require any variation to any part of the Works the same shall be deemed to have been given pursuant to Clause 51.

*Clause amended to indicate addition of profit to cost in respect of any additional permanent or temporary work.*

**Programme to be furnished**

**14** (1) (a) Within 21 days after the award of the Contract the Contractor shall submit to the Engineer for his acceptance a programme showing the order in which he proposes to carry out the Works having regard to the provisions of Clause 42(1).

(b) At the same time the Contractor shall also provide in writing for the information of the Engineer a general description of the arrangements and methods of construction which the Contractor proposes to adopt for the carrying out of the Works.

(c) Should the Engineer reject any programme under sub-clause (2)(b) of this Clause the Contractor shall within 21 days of such rejection submit a revised programme.

*New sub-clause requiring the Contractor to submit a revised programme should any programme be rejected.*

**Action by Engineer**

(2) The Engineer shall within 21 days after receipt of the Contractor's programme

(a) accept the programme in writing or

(b) reject the programme in writing with reasons or

(c) request the Contractor to supply further information to clarify or substantiate the programme or to satisfy the Engineer as to its reasonableness having regard to the Contractor's obligations under the Contract.

Provided that if none of the above actions is taken within the said period of 21 days the Engineer shall be deemed to have accepted the programme as submitted.

**Revision of Programme.**

(2) Should it appear to the Engineer at any time that the actual progress of the Works does not conform with the approved programme referred to in sub-clause (1) of this Clause the Engineer shall be entitled to require the Contractor to produce a revised programme showing the modifications to the original programme necessary to ensure completion of the Works or any Section within the time for completion as defined in Clause 43 or extended time granted pursuant to Clause 44(2).

**Methods of Construction.**

(3) If requested by the Engineer the Contractor shall submit at such times and in such detail as the Engineer may reasonably require such information pertaining to the methods of construction (including Temporary Works and the use of Constructional Plant) which the Contractor proposes to adopt or use and such calculations of stresses strains and deflections that will arise in the Permanent Works or any parts thereof during construction from the use of such methods as will enable the Engineer to decide whether if these methods are adhered to the Works can be executed in accordance with the Drawings and Specification and without detriment to the Permanent Works when completed.

**Engineer's Consent.**

(4) The Engineer shall inform the Contractor in writing within a reasonable period after receipt of the information submitted in accordance with sub-clause (3) of this Clause either:—

    (a) that the Contractor's proposed methods have the consent of the Engineer; or
    (b) in what respects in the opinion of the Engineer they fail to meet the requirements of the Drawings or Specification or will be detrimental to the Permanent Works.

In the latter event the Contractor shall take such steps or make such changes in the said methods as may be necessary to meet the Engineer's requirements and to obtain his consent. The Contractor shall not change the methods which have received the Engineer's consent without the further consent in writing of the Engineer which shall not be unreasonably withheld.

**Design Criteria.**

(5) The Engineer shall provide to the Contractor such design criteria relevant to the Permanent Works or any Temporary Works designed by the Engineer as may be necessary to enable the Contractor to comply with sub-clauses (3) and (4) of this Clause.

36

*New Clause placing a time limit of 21 days on the action by the Engineer following receipt of the Contractor's programme. Failing any action within 21 days the programme as submitted is deemed to have been accepted.*

**Provision of further information**

(3)   The Contractor shall within 21 days after receiving from the Engineer any request under sub-clause (2)(c) of this Clause or within such further period as the Engineer may allow provide the further information requested failing which the relevant programme shall be deemed to be rejected.

Upon receipt of such further information the Engineer shall within a further 21 days accept or reject the programme in accordance with sub-clauses (2)(a) or (2)(b) of this Clause.

*New Clause under which the Contractor can be required to provide additional information before the Engineer makes his decision regarding the acceptance or rejection of the Contractor's programme.*

**Revision of programme**

(4)   Should it appear to the Engineer at any time that the actual progress of the work does not conform with the accepted programme referred to in sub-clause (1) of this Clause the Engineer shall be entitled to require the Contractor to produce a revised programme showing such modifications to the original programme as may be necessary to ensure completion of the Works or any Section within the time for completion as defined in Clause 43 or extended time granted pursuant to Clause 44. In such event the Contractor shall submit his revised programme within 21 days or within such further period as the Engineer shall allow. Thereafter the provisions of sub-clauses (2) and (3) of this Clause shall apply.

*As previous Clause 14(2) but with the addition of 21 day time limits for both the submission of the revised programme by the Contractor and for the Engineer's acceptance.*

**Design criteria**

(5)   The Engineer shall provide to the Contractor such design criteria relevant to the Permanent Works or any Temporary Works design supplied by the Engineer as may be necessary to enable the Contractor to comply with sub-clauses (6) and (7) of this Clause.

**Methods of construction**

(6)   If requested by the Engineer the Contractor shall submit at such times and in such further detail as the Engineer may reasonably require information pertaining to the methods of construction (including Temporary Works and the use of Contractor's Equipment) which the Contractor proposes to adopt or use and calculations of stresses strains and deflections that will arise in the Permanent Works or any parts thereof during construction so as to enable the Engineer to decide whether if these methods are adhered to the Works can be constructed and completed in accordance with the Contract and without detriment to the Permanent Works when completed.

**Engineer's consent**

(7)   The Engineer shall inform the Contractor in writing within 21 days after receipt of the information submitted in accordance with sub-clauses (1)(b) and (6) of this Clause either

(a)   that the Contractor's proposed methods have the consent of the Engineer or

(b)   in what respects in the opinion of the Engineer they fail to meet the requirements of the Contract or will be detrimental to the Permanent Works.

**Delay and Extra Cost.**

(6) If the Engineer's consent to the proposed methods of construction shall be unreasonably delayed or if the requirements of the Engineer pursuant to sub-clause (4) of this Clause or any limitations imposed by any of the design criteria supplied by the Engineer pursuant to sub-clause (5) of this Clause could not reasonably have been foreseen by an experienced contractor at the time of tender and if in consequence of any of the aforesaid the Contractor unavoidably incurs delay or cost the Engineer shall take such delay into account in determining any extension of time to which the Contractor is entitled under Clause 44 and the Contractor shall subject to Clause 52(4) be paid in accordance with Clause 60 such sum in respect of the cost incurred as the Engineer considers fair in all the circumstances.

**Responsibility Unaffected by Approval.**

(7) Approval by the Engineer of the Contractor's programme in accordance with sub-clauses (1) and (2) of this Clause and the consent of the Engineer to the Contractor's proposed methods of construction in accordance with sub-clause (4) of this Clause shall not relieve the Contractor of any of his duties or responsibilities under the Contract.

**Contractor's Superintendence.**

**15.** (1) The Contractor shall give or provide all necessary superintendence during the execution of the Works and as long thereafter as the Engineer may consider necessary. Such superintendence shall be given by sufficient persons having adequate knowledge of the operations to be carried out (including the methods and techniques required the hazards likely to be encountered and methods of preventing accidents) as may be requisite for the satisfactory construction of the Works.

**Contractor's Agent.**

(2) The Contractor or a competent and authorised agent or representative approved of in writing by the Engineer (which approval may at any time be withdrawn) is to be constantly on the Works and shall give his whole time to the superintendence of the same. Such authorised agent or representative shall be in full charge of the Works and shall receive on behalf of the Contractor directions and instructions from the Engineer or (subject to the limitations of Clause 2) the Engineer's Representative. The Contractor or such authorised agent or representative shall be responsible for the safety of all operations.

**Removal of Contractor's Employees.**

**16.** The Contractor shall employ or cause to be employed in and about the execution of the Works and in the superintendence thereof only such persons as are careful skilled and experienced in their several trades and callings and the Engineer shall be at liberty to object to and require the Contractor to remove from the Works any person employed by the Contractor in or about the execution of the Works who in the opinion of the Engineer misconducts himself or is incompetent

In the latter event the Contractor shall take such steps or make such changes in the said methods as may be necessary to meet the Engineer's requirements and to obtain his consent. The Contractor shall not change the methods which have received the Engineer's consent without the further consent in writing of the Engineer which shall not be unreasonably withheld.

*Substantially as previous Clause 14(4) this Clause now also applies to the proposed methods of construction outlined by the Contractor under Clause 14(1)(b).*

**Delay and cost**

(8)   If the Contractor unavoidably incurs delay or cost because

(a)   the Engineer's consent to the proposed methods of construction is unreasonably delayed or

(b)   the Engineer's requirements pursuant to sub-clause (7) of this Clause or any limitations imposed by any of the design criteria supplied by the Engineer pursuant to sub-clause (5) of this Clause could not reasonably have been foreseen by an experienced contractor at the time of tender

the Engineer shall take such delay into account in determining any extension of time to which the Contractor is entitled under Clause 44 and the Contractor shall subject to Clause 52(4) be paid in accordance with Clause 60 such sum in respect of the cost incurred as the Engineer considers fair in all the circumstances. Profit shall be added thereto in respect of any additional permanent or temporary work.

*Clause amended to indicate addition of profit to cost in respect of any additional permanent or temporary work.*

**Responsibility unaffected by acceptance or consent**

(9)   Acceptance by the Engineer of the Contractor's programme in accordance with sub-clauses (2)(3) or (4) of this Clause and the consent of the Engineer to the Contractor's proposed methods of construction in accordance with sub-clause (7) of this Clause shall not relieve the Contractor of any of his duties or responsibilities under the Contract.

**Contractor's superintendence**

15   (1)   The Contractor shall give or provide all necessary superintendence during the construction and completion of the Works and as long thereafter as the Engineer may consider necessary. Such superintendence shall be given by sufficient persons having adequate knowledge of the operations to be carried out (including the methods and techniques required the hazards likely to be encountered and methods of preventing accidents) as may be requisite for the satisfactory and safe construction of the Works.

**Contractor's agent**

(2)   The Contractor or a competent and authorized agent or representative approved of in writing by the Engineer (which approval may at any time be withdrawn) is to be constantly on the Works and shall give his whole time to the superintendence of the same. Such authorized agent or representative shall be in full charge of the Works and shall receive on behalf of the Contractor directions and instructions from the Engineer or (subject to the limitations of Clause 2) the Engineer's Representative. The Contractor or such authorized agent or representative shall be responsible for the safety of all operations.

**Removal of Contractor's employees**

16   The Contractor shall employ or cause to be employed in and about the construction and completion of the Works and in the superintendence thereof only such persons as are careful skilled and experienced in their several trades and callings.

39

or negligent in the performance of his duties or fails to conform with any particular provisions with regard to safety which may be set out in the Specification or persists in any conduct which is prejudicial to safety or health and such persons shall not be again employed upon the Works without the permission of the Engineer.

**Setting-out.**

17. The Contractor shall be responsible for the true and proper setting-out of the Works and for the correctness of the position levels dimensions and alignment of all parts of the Works and for the provision of all necessary instruments appliances and labour in connection therewith. If at any time during the progress of the Works any error shall appear or arise in the position levels dimensions or alignment of any part of the Works the Contractor on being required so to do by the Engineer shall at his own cost rectify such error to the satisfaction of the Engineer unless such error is based on incorrect data supplied in writing by the Engineer or the Engineer's Representative in which case the cost of rectifying the same shall be borne by the Employer. The checking of any setting-out or of any line or level by the Engineer or the Engineer's Representative shall not in any way relieve the Contractor of his responsibility for the correctness thereof and the Contractor shall carefully protect and preserve all bench-marks sight rails pegs and other things used in setting out the Works.

**Boreholes and Exploratory Excavation.**

18. If at any time during the execution of the Works the Engineer shall require the Contractor to make boreholes or to carry out exploratory excavation such requirement shall be ordered in writing and shall be deemed to be a variation ordered under Clause 51 unless a Provisional Sum or Prime Cost Item in respect of such anticipated work shall have been included in the Bill of Quantities.

**Safety and Security.**

19. (1) The Contractor shall throughout the progress of the Works have full regard for the safety of all persons entitled to be upon the Site and shall keep the Site (so far as the same is under his control) and the Works (so far as the same are not completed or occupied by the Employer) in an orderly state appropriate to the avoidance of danger to such persons and shall *inter alia* in connection with the Works provide and maintain at his own cost all lights guards fencing warning signs and watching when and where necessary or required by the Engineer or by any competent statutory or other authority for the protection of the Works or for the safety and convenience of the public or others.

**Employer's Responsibilities.**

(2) If under Clause 31 the Employer shall carry out work on the Site with his own workmen he shall in respect of such work:—

(a) have full regard to the safety of all persons entitled to be upon the Site; and
(b) keep the Site in an orderly state appropriate to the avoidance of danger to such persons.

If under Clause 31 the Employer shall employ other contractors on the Site he shall require them to have the same regard for safety and avoidance of danger.

The Engineer shall be at liberty to object to and require the Contractor to remove or cause to be removed from the Works any person employed thereon who in the opinion of the Engineer misconducts himself or is incompetent or negligent in the performance of his duties or fails to conform with any particular provisions with regard to safety which may be set out in the Contract or persists in any conduct which is prejudicial to safety or health and such persons shall not be again employed upon the Works without the permission of the Engineer.

**Setting-out** 17 (1) The Contractor shall be responsible for the true and proper setting-out of the Works and for the correctness of the position levels dimensions and alignment of all parts of the Works and for the provision of all necessary instruments appliances and labour in connection therewith.

(2) If at any time during the progress of the Works any error shall appear or arise in the position levels dimensions or alignment of any part of the Works the Contractor on being required so to do by the Engineer shall at his own cost rectify such error to the satisfaction of the Engineer unless such error is based on incorrect data supplied in writing by the Engineer or the Engineer's Representative in which case the cost of rectifying the same shall be borne by the Employer.

(3) The checking of any setting-out or of any line or level by the Engineer or the Engineer's Representative shall not in any way relieve the Contractor of his responsiblity for the correctness thereof and the Contractor shall carefully protect and preserve all bench-marks sight rails pegs and other things used in setting out the Works.

**Boreholes and exploratory excavation** 18 If at any time during the construction of the Works the Engineer shall require the Contractor to make boreholes or to carry out exploratory excavation such requirement shall be ordered in writing and shall be deemed to be a variation under Clause 51 unless a Provisional Sum or Prime Cost Item in respect of such anticipated work shall have been included in the Bill of Quantities.

**Safety and security** 19 (1) The Contractor shall throughout the progress of the Works have full regard for the safety of all persons entitled to be upon the Site and shall keep the Site (so far as the same is under his control) and the Works (so far as the same are not completed or occupied by the Employer) in an orderly state appropriate to the avoidance of danger to such persons and shall inter alia in connection with the Works provide and maintain at his own cost all lights guards fencing warning signs and watching when and where necessary or required by the Engineer or the Engineer's Representative or by any competent statutory or other authority for the protection of the Works or for the safety and convenience of the public or others.

*Clause extended to cover requirements of the Engineer's Representative.*

**Employer's responsibilities** (2) If under Clause 31 the Employer shall carry out work on the Site with his own workmen he shall in respect of such work

(a) have full regard to the safety of all persons entitled to be upon the Site and

(b) keep the Site in an orderly state appropriate to the avoidance of danger to such persons.

If under Clause 31 the Employer shall employ other contractors on the Site he shall require them to have the same regard for safety and avoidance of danger.

**Care of the Works.**

20. (1) The Contractor shall take full responsibility for the care of the Works from the date of the commencement thereof until 14 days after the Engineer shall have issued a Certificate of Completion for the whole of the Works pursuant to Clause 48. Provided that if the Engineer shall issue a Certificate of Completion in respect of any Section or part of the Permanent Works before he shall issue a Certificate of Completion in respect of the whole of the Works the Contractor shall cease to be responsible for the care of that Section or part of the Permanent Works 14 days after the Engineer shall have issued the Certificate of Completion in respect of that Section or part and the responsibility for the care thereof shall thereupon pass to the Employer. Provided further that the Contractor shall take full responsibility for the care of any outstanding work which he shall have undertaken to finish during the Period of Maintenance until such outstanding work is complete.

**Responsibility for Reinstatement.**

(2) In case any damage loss or injury from any cause whatsoever (save and except the Excepted Risks as defined in sub-clause (3) of this Clause) shall happen to the Works or any part thereof while the Contractor shall be responsible for the care thereof the Contractor shall at his own cost repair and make good the same so that at completion the Permanent Works shall be in good order and condition and in conformity in every respect with the requirements of the Contract and the Engineer's instructions. To the extent that any such damage loss or injury arises from any of the Excepted Risks the Contractor shall if required by the Engineer repair and make good the same as aforesaid at the expense of the Employer. The Contractor shall also be liable for any damage to the Works occasioned by him in the course of any operations carried out by him for the purpose of completing any outstanding work or of complying with his obligations under Clauses 49 and 50.

**Excepted Risks.**

(3) The " Excepted Risks " are riot war invasion act of foreign enemies hostilities (whether war be declared or not) civil war rebellion revolution insurrection or military or usurped power ionising radiations or contamination by radio-activity from any nuclear fuel or from any nuclear waste from the combustion of nuclear fuel radioactive toxic explosive or other hazardous properties of any explosive nuclear assembly or nuclear component thereof pressure waves caused by aircraft or other aerial devices travelling at sonic or supersonic speeds or a cause due to use or occupation by the Employer his agents servants or other contractors (not being employed by the Contractor) of any part of the Permanent Works or to fault defect error or omission in the design of the Works (other than a design provided by the Contractor pursuant to his obligations under the Contract).

**Care of the Works**

**20** (1) (a) The Contractor shall save as in paragraph (b) hereof and subject to sub-clause (2) of this Clause take full responsibility for the care of the Works and materials plant and equipment for incorporation therein from the Works Commencement Date until the date of issue of a Certificate of Substantial Completion for the whole of the Works when the responsibility for the said care shall pass to the Employer.

(b) If the Engineer issues a Certificate of Substantial Completion for any Section or part of the Permanent Works the Contractor shall cease to be responsible for the care of that Section or part from the date of issue of such Certificate of Substantial Completion when the responsibility for the care of that Section or part shall pass to the Employer.

(c) The Contractor shall take full responsibility for the care of any outstanding work and materials plant and equipment for incorporation therein which he undertakes to finish during the Defects Correction Period until such outstanding work has been completed.

*The Contractor's responsibilities now cease on issue of the Certificate of Substantial Completion except in respect of outstanding work, searches or rectifications to be completed during or after the expiry of the Defects Correction Period.*

**Excepted Risks**

(2) The Excepted Risks for which the Contractor is not liable are loss or damage to the extent that it is due to

(a) the use or occupation by the Employer his agents servants or other contractors (not being employed by the Contractor) of any part of the Permanent Works

(b) any fault defect error or omission in the design of the Works (other than a design provided by the Contractor pursuant to his obligations under the Contract)

(c) riot war invasion act of foreign enemies or hostilities (whether war be declared or not)

(d) civil war rebellion revolution insurrection or military or usurped power

(e) ionizing radiations or contamination by radioactivity from any nuclear fuel or from any nuclear waste from the combustion of nuclear fuel radioactive toxic explosive or other hazardous properties of any explosive nuclear assembly or nuclear component thereof and

(f) pressure waves caused by aircraft or other aerial devices travelling at sonic or supersonic speeds.

**Rectification of loss or damage**

(3) (a) In the event of any loss or damage to

(i) the Works or any Section or part thereof or
(ii) materials plant or equipment for incorporation therein

while the Contractor is responsible for the care thereof (except as provided in sub-clause (2) of this Clause) the Contractor shall at his own cost rectify such loss or damage so that the Permanent Works conform in every respect with the provisions of the Contract and the Engineers's instructions. The Contractor shall also be liable for any loss or damage to the Works occasioned by him in the course of any operations carried out by him for the purpose of complying with his obligations under Clauses 49 and 50.

**Insurance of Works, etc.**

**21.** Without limiting his obligations and responsibilities under Clause 20 the Contractor shall insure in the joint names of the Employer and the Contractor:—

    (a)  the Permanent Works and the Temporary Works (including for the purposes of this Clause any unfixed materials or other things delivered to the Site for incorporation therein) to their full value;

    (b)  the Constructional Plant to its full value;

against all loss or damage from whatever cause arising (other than the Excepted Risks) for which he is responsible under the terms of the Contract and in such manner that the Employer and Contractor are covered for the period stipulated in Clause 20(1) and are also covered for loss or damage arising during the Period of Maintenance from such cause occurring prior to the commencement of the Period of Maintenance and for any loss or damage occasioned by the Contractor in the course of any operation carried out by him for the purpose of complying with his obligations under Clauses 49 and 50.

Provided that without limiting his obligations and responsibilities as aforesaid nothing in this Clause contained shall render the Contractor liable to insure against the necessity for the repair or reconstruction of any work constructed with materials and workmanship not in accordance with the requirements of the Contract unless the Bill of Quantities shall provide a special item for this insurance.

Such insurances shall be effected with an insurer and in terms approved by the Employer (which approval shall not be unreasonably withheld) and the Contractor shall whenever required produce to the Employer the policy or policies of insurance and the receipts for payment of the current premiums.

**Damage to Persons and Property.**

**22.** (1) The Contractor shall (except if and so far as the Contract otherwise provides) indemnify and keep indemnified the Employer against all losses and claims for injuries or damage to any person or property whatsoever (other than the Works for which insurance is required under Clause 21 but including surface or other damage to land being the Site suffered by any persons in beneficial occupation of such land) which may arise out of or in consequence of the construction and maintenance of the Works and against all claims demands proceedings damages costs charges and expenses whatsoever in respect thereof or in relation thereto. Provided always that:—

(b)   Should any such loss or damage arise from any of the Excepted Risks defined in sub-clause (2) of this Clause the Contractor shall if and to the extent required by the Engineer rectify the loss or damage at the expense of the Employer.

(c)   In the event of loss or damage arising from an Excepted Risk and a risk for which the Contractor is responsible under sub-clause (1)(a) of this Clause then the Engineer shall when determining the expense to be borne by the Employer under the Contract apportion the cost of rectification into that part caused by the Excepted Risk and that part which is the responsibility of the Contractor.

*This sub-clause makes provision for the apportionment of the cost of rectification if part is caused by an Excepted Risk and part is the responsibility of the Contractor.*

**Insurance of Works etc.**

21   (1)   The Contractor shall without limiting his or the Employers obligations and responsibilities under Clause 20 insure in the joint names of the Contractor and the Employer the Works together with materials plant and equipment for incorporation therein to the full replacement cost plus an additional 10% to cover any additional costs that may arise incidental to the rectification of any loss or damage including professional fees cost of demolition and removal of debris.

*Substantially as the first part of previous Clause 21 but to be to the full replacement cost to which is added an additional 10% to cover any additional costs. The contractual obligation to insure the Contractor's Equipment is now omitted.*

**Extent of cover**

(2)   (a)   The insurance required under sub-clause (1) of this Clause shall cover the Employer and the Contractor against all loss or damage from whatsoever cause arising other than the Excepted Risks defined in Clause 20 (2) from the Works Commencement Date until the date of issue of the relevant Certificate of Substantial Completion.

(b)   The insurance shall extend to cover any loss or damage arising during the Defects Correction Period from a cause occuring prior to the issue of any Certificate of Substantial Completion and any loss or damage occasioned by the Contractor in the course of any operation carried out by him for the purpose of complying with his obligations under Clauses 49 and 50.

(c)   Nothing in this Clause shall render the Contractor liable to insure against the necessity for the repair or reconstruction of any work constructed with materials or workmanship not in accordance with the requirements of the Contract unless the Bill of Quantities shall provide a special item for this insurance.

(d)   Any amounts not insured or not recovered from insurers whether as excesses carried under the policy or otherwise shall be borne by the Contractor or the Employer in accordance with their respective responsibilities under Clause 20.

*New sub-clause covering shared responsibility.*

**Damage to persons and property**

22   (1)   The Contractor shall except if and so far as the Contract provides otherwise and subject to the exceptions set out in sub-clause (2) of this Clause indemnify and keep indemnified the Employer against all losses and claims in respect of

(a)   death of or injury to any person or

(b)   loss of or damage to any property (other than the Works)

45

(a) the Contractor's liability to indemnify the Employer as aforesaid shall be reduced proportionately to the extent that the act or neglect of the Employer his servants or agents may have contributed to the said loss injury or damage;

(b) nothing herein contained shall be deemed to render the Contractor liable for or in respect of or to indemnify the Employer against any compensation or damages for or with respect to:—

    (i) damage to crops being on the Site (save in so far as possession has not been given to the Contractor);

    (ii) the use or occupation of land (which has been provided by the Employer) by the Works or any part thereof or for the purpose of constructing completing and maintaining the Works (including consequent losses of crops) or interference whether temporary or permanent with any right of way light air or water or other easement or quasi easement which are the unavoidable result of the construction of the Works in accordance with the Contract;

    (iii) the right of the Employer to construct the Works or any part thereof on over under in or through any land;

    (iv) damage which is the unavoidable result of the construction of the Works in accordance with the Contract;

    (v) injuries or damage to persons or property resulting from any act or neglect or breach of statutory duty done or committed by the Engineer or the Employer his agents servants or other contractors (not being employed by the Contractor) or for or in respect of any claims demands proceedings damages costs charges and expenses in respect thereof or in relation thereto.

**Indemnity by Employer.**

(2) The Employer will save harmless and indemnify the Contractor from and against all claims demands proceedings damages costs charges and expenses in respect of the matters referred to in the proviso to sub-clause (1) of this Clause. Provided always that the Employer's liability to indemnify the Contractor under paragraph (v) of proviso (b) to sub-clause (1) of this Clause shall be reduced proportionately to the extent that the act or neglect of the Contractor or his sub-contractors servants or agents may have contributed to the said injury or damage.

**Insurance against Damage to Persons and Property.**

23. (1) Throughout the execution of the Works the Contractor (but without limiting his obligations and responsibilities under Clause 22) shall insure against any damage loss or injury which may occur to any property or to any person by or arising out of the execution of the Works or in the carrying out of the Contract otherwise than due to the matters referred to in proviso (b) to Clause 22(1).

**Amount and Terms of Insurance.**

(2) Such insurance shall be effected with an insurer and in terms approved by the Employer (which approval shall not be unreasonably withheld) and for at least the amount stated in the Appendix to the Form of Tender. The terms shall include a provision whereby in the event of any claim in respect of which the Contractor would be entitled to receive indemnity under the policy being brought or made against the Employer the insurer will indemnify the Employer against such claims and any costs charges and expenses in respect thereof. The Contractor shall whenever required produce to the Employer the policy or policies of insurance and the receipts for payment of the current premiums.

which may arise out of or in consequence of the execution of the Works and the remedying of any defects therein and against all claims demands proceedings damages costs charges and expenses whatsoever in respect thereof or in relation thereto.

**Exceptions**

(2)  The exceptions referred to in sub-clause (1) of this Clause which are the responsibility of the Employer are

(a)  damage to crops being on the Site (save in so far as possession has not been given to the Contractor)

(b)  the use or occupation of land (provided by the Employer) by the Works or any part thereof or for the purpose of executing and maintaining the Works (including consequent losses of crops) or interference whether temporary or permanent with any right of way light air or water or other easement or quasi-easement which are the unavoidable result of the construction of the Works in accordance with the Contract

(c)  the right of the Employer to construct the Works or any part thereof on over under in or through any land

(d)  damage which is the unavoidable result of the construction of the Works in accordance with the Contract and

(e)  death of or injury to persons or loss of or damage to property resulting from any act neglect or breach of statutory duty done or committed by the Employer his agents servants or other contractors (not being employed by the Contractor) or for or in respect of any claims demands proceedings damages costs charges and expenses in respect thereof or in relation thereto.

**Indemnity by Employer**

(3)  The Employer shall subject to sub-clause (4) of this Clause indemnify the Contractor against all claims demands proceedings damages costs charges and expenses in respect of the matters referred to in the exceptions defined in sub-clause (2)of this Clause.

**Shared responsibility**

(4)  (a)  The Contractor's liability to indemnify the Employer under sub-clause (1) of this Clause shall be reduced in proportion to the extent that the act or neglect of the Employer his agents servants or other contractors (not being employed by the Contractor) may have contributed to the said death injury loss or damage.

(b)  The Employer's liability to indemnify the Contractor under sub-clause (3) of this Clause in respect of matters referred to in sub-clause (2)(e) of this Clause shall be reduced in proportion to the extent that the act or neglect of the Contractor or his sub-contractors servants or agents may have contributed to the said death injury loss or damage.

**Third party insurance**

**23**  (1)  The Contractor shall without limiting his or the Employer's obligations and responsibilities under Clause 22 insure in the joint names of the Contractor and the Employer against liabilities for death of or injury to any person (other than any operative or other person in the employment of the Contractor or any of his sub-contractors) or loss of or damage to any property (other than the Works) arising out of the execution of the Contract other than the exceptions defined in Clause 22(2)(a)(b)(c) and (d).

**Cross liability clause**

(2)  The insurance policy shall include a cross liability clause such that the insurance shall apply to the Contractor and to the Employer as separate insured.

**Amount of insurance**

(3)  Such insurance shall be for at least the amount stated in the Appendix to the Form of Tender.

**Accident or Injury to Workmen.**

**24.** The Employer shall not be liable for or in respect of any damages or compensation payable at law in respect or in consequence of any accident or injury to any workman or other person in the employment of the Contractor or any sub-contractor save and except to the extent that such accident or injury results from or is contributed to by any act or default of the Employer his agents or servants and the Contractor shall indemnify and keep indemnified the Employer against all such damages and compensation (save and except as aforesaid) and against all claims demands proceedings costs charges and expenses whatsoever in respect thereof or in relation thereto.

**Remedy on Contractor's Failure to Insure.**

**25.** If the Contractor shall fail upon request to produce to the Employer satisfactory evidence that there is in force the insurance referred to in Clauses 21 and 23 or any other insurance which he may be required to effect under the terms of the Contract then and in any such case the Employer may effect and keep in force any such insurance and pay such premium or premiums as may be necessary for that purpose and from time to time deduct the amount so paid by the Employer as aforesaid from any monies due or which may become due to the Contractor or recover the same as a debt due from the Contractor.

**Giving of Notices and Payment of Fees.**

**26.** (1) The Contractor shall save as provided in Clause 27 give all notices and pay all fees required to be given or paid by any Act of Parliament or any Regulation or Bye-law of any local or other statutory authority in relation to the execution of the Works and by the rules and regulations of all public bodies and companies whose property or rights are or may be affected in any way by the Works. The Employer shall repay or allow to the Contractor all such sums as the Engineer shall certify to have been properly payable and paid by the Contractor in respect of such fees and also all rates and taxes paid by the Contractor in respect of the Site or any part thereof or anything constructed or erected thereon or on any part thereof or any temporary structures situate elsewhere but used exclusively for the purposes of the Works or any structures used temporarily and exclusively for the purposes of the Works.

*Third party insurance is now to be in the joint names with a cross-liability clause so that the insurance applies to the Contractor and the Employer as separate insured.*

**Accident or injury to workpeople**

**24** The Employer shall not be liable for or in respect of any damages or compensation payable at law in respect or in consequence of any accident or injury to any operative or other person in the employment of the Contractor or any of his sub-contractors save and except to the extent that such accident or injury results from or is contributed to by any act or default of the Employer his agents or servants and the Contractor shall indemnify and keep indemnified the Employer against all such damages and compensation (save and except as aforesaid) and against all claims demands proceedings costs charges and expenses whatsoever in respect thereof or in relation thereto.

**Evidence and terms of insurance**

**25** (1) The Contractor shall provide satisfactory evidence to the Employer prior to the Works Commencement Date that the insurances required under the Contract have been effected and shall if so required produce the insurance policies for inspection. The terms of all such insurances shall be subject to the approval of the Employer (which approval shall not unreasonably be withheld). The Contractor shall upon request produce to the Employer receipts for the payment of current insurance premiums.

*The Contractor is now required to provide satisfactory evidence of insurances prior to the Works Commencement Date.*

**Excesses**

(2) Any excesses on the policies of insurance effected under Clauses 21 and 23 shall be as stated by the Contractor in the Appendix to the Form of Tender.

*The Contractor now has to state in the Appendix to the Form of Tender the excesses carried on his insurance policies.*

**Remedy on Contractor's failure to insure**

(3) If the Contractor shall fail upon request to produce to the Employer satisfactory evidence that there is in force any of the insurances required under the Contract then and in any such case the Employer may effect and keep in force any such insurance and pay such premium or premiums as may be necessary for that purpose and from time to time deduct the amount so paid from any monies due or which may become due to the Contractor or recover the same as a debt due from the Contractor.

**Compliance with policy conditions**

(4) Both the Employer and the Contractor shall comply with all conditions laid down in the insurance policies. In the event that the Contractor or the Employer fails to comply with any condition imposed by the insurance policies effected pursuant to the Contract each shall indemnify the other against all losses and claims arising from such failure.

*New Clause.*

**Giving of notices and payment of fees**

**26** (1) The Contractor shall save as provided in Clause 27 give all notices and pay all fees required to be given or paid by any Act of Parliament or any Regulation or Bye-law of any local or other statutory authority in relation to the construction and completion of the Works and by the rules and regulations of all public bodies and companies whose property or rights are or may be affected in any way by the Works.

**Contractor to Conform with Statutes, etc.**

(2) The Contractor shall ascertain and conform in all respects with the provisions of any general or local Act of Parliament and the Regulations and Bye-laws of any local or other statutory authority which may be applicable to the Works and with such rules and regulations of public bodies and companies as aforesaid and shall keep the Employer indemnified against all penalties and liability of every kind for breach of any such Act Regulation or Bye-law. Provided always that:—

(a) the Contractor shall not be required to indemnify the Employer against the consequences of any such breach which is the unavoidable result of complying with the Drawings Specification or instructions of the Engineer;

(b) if the Drawings Specification or instructions of the Engineer shall at any time be found not to be in conformity with any such Act Regulation or Bye-law the Engineer shall issue such instructions including the ordering of a variation under Clause 51 as may be necessary to ensure conformity with such Act Regulation or Bye-law;

(c) the Contractor shall not be responsible for obtaining any planning permission which may be necessary in respect of the Permanent Works or any Temporary Works specified or designed by the Engineer and the Employer hereby warrants that all the said permissions have been or will in due time be obtained.

**Public Utilities Street Works Act 1950— Definitions.**

27. (1) For the purposes of this Clause:—

(a) the expression " the Act " shall mean and include the Public Utilities Street Works Act 1950 and any statutory modification or re-enactment thereof for the time being in force;

(b) all other expressions common to the Act and to this Clause shall have the same meaning as that assigned to them by the Act.

**Notifications by Employer to Contractor.**

(2) The Employer shall before the commencement of the Works notify the Contractor in writing:—

(a) whether the Works or any parts thereof (and if so which parts) are Emergency Works; and

(b) which (if any) parts of the Works are to be carried out in Controlled Land or in a Prospectively Maintainable Highway.

If any duly authorised variation of the Works shall involve the execution thereof in a Street or in Controlled Land or in a Prospectively Maintainable Highway or are Emergency Works the Employer shall notify the Contractor in writing accordingly at the time such variation is ordered.

**Service of Notices by Employer.**

(3) The Employer shall (subject to the obligations of the Contractor under sub-clause (4) of this Clause) serve all such notices as may from time to time whether before or during the course of or after completion of the Works be required to be served under the Act.

**Repayment by Employer**

(2) The Employer shall repay or allow to the Contractor all such sums as the Engineer shall certify to have been properly payable and paid by the Contractor in respect of such fees and also all rates and taxes paid by the Contractor in respect of the Site or any part thereof or anything constructed or erected thereon or on any part thereof or any temporary structures situated elsewhere but used exclusively for the purposes of the Works or any structures used temporarily and exclusively for the purposes of the Works.

**Contractor to conform with Statutes etc.**

(3) The Contractor shall ascertain and conform in all respects with the provisions of any general or local Act of Parliament and the Regulations and Bye-laws of any local or other statutory authority which may be applicable to the Works and with such rules and regulations of public bodies and companies as aforesaid and shall keep the Employer indemnified against all penalties and liability of every kind for breach of any such Act Regulation or Bye-law. Provided always that

(a) the Contractor shall not be required to indemnify the Employer against the consequences of any such breach which is the unavoidable result of complying with the Contract or instructions of the Engineer

(b) if the Contract or instructions of the Engineer shall at any time be found not to be in conformity with any such Act Regulation or Bye-law the Engineer shall issue such instructions including the ordering of a variation under Clause 51 as may be necessary to ensure conformity with such Act Regulation or Bye-law and

(c) the Contractor shall not be responsible for obtaining any planning permission which may be necessary in respect of the Permanent Works or any Temporary Works design supplied by the Engineer and the Employer hereby warrants that all the said permissions have been or will in due time be obtained.

**Public Utilities Street Works Act 1950—definitions**

27 (1) For the purposes of this Clause

(a) the expression "the Act" shall mean and include the Public Utilities Street Works Act 1950 and any statutory modification or re-enactment thereof for the time being in force and

(b) all other expressions common to the Act and to this Clause shall have the same meaning as those assigned to them by the Act.

**Notifications by Employer to Contractor**

(2) (a) The Employer shall before the commencement of the Works notify the Contractor in writing

(i) whether the Works or any parts thereof (and if so which parts) are Emergency Works and

(ii) which (if any) parts of the Works are to be carried out in Controlled Land or in a Prospectively Maintainable Highway.

(b) If any duly authorized variation of the Works shall involve the execution thereof in a Street or in Controlled Land or in a Prospectively Maintainable Highway or are Emergency Works the Employer shall notify the Contractor in writing accordingly at the time such variation is ordered.

**Service of notices by Employer**

(3) The Employer shall (subject to the obligations of the Contractor under sub-clause (4) of this Clause) serve all such notices as may from time to time whether before or during the course of or after completion of the Works be required to be served under the Act.

**Notices by Contractor to Employer.**

(4)   The Contractor shall in relation to any part of the Works (other than Emergency Works) and subject to the compliance by the Employer with sub-clause (2) of this Clause give not less than 21 days' notice in writing to the Employer before:—

(a)   commencing any part of the Works in a Street (as defined by Sections 1(3) and 38(1) of the Act); or

(b)   commencing any part of the Works in Controlled Land or in a Prospectively Maintainable Highway; or

(c)   commencing in a Street or in Controlled Land or in a Prospectively Maintainable Highway any part of the Works which is likely to affect the apparatus of any Owning Undertaker (within the meaning of Section 26 of the Act).

Such notice shall state the date on which and the place at which the Contractor intends to commence the execution of the work referred to therein.

**Failure to Commence Street Works.**

(5)   If the Contractor having given any such notice as is required by sub-clause (4) of this Clause shall not commence the part of the Works to which such notice relates within 2 months after the date when such notice is given such notice shall be treated as invalid and compliance with the said sub-clause (4) shall be requisite as if such notice had not been given.

**Delays Attributable to Variations.**

(6)   In the event of such a variation of the Works as is referred to in sub-clause (2) of this Clause being ordered by or on behalf of the Employer and resulting in delay in the execution of the Works by reason of the necessity of compliance by the Contractor with sub-clause (4) of this Clause the Engineer shall take such delay into account in determining any extension of time to which the Contractor is entitled under Clause 44 and the Contractor shall subject to Clause 52 be paid in accordance with Clause 60 such additional cost as the Engineer shall consider to have been reasonably attributable to such delay.

**Contractor to Comply with Other Obligations of Act.**

(7)   Except as otherwise provided by this Clause where in relation to the carrying out of the Works the Act imposes any requirements or obligations upon the Employer the Contractor shall subject to Clause 49(5) comply with such requirements and obligations and shall (subject as aforesaid) indemnify the Employer against any liability which the Employer may incur in consequence of any failure to comply with the said requirements and obligations.

**Patent Rights.**

28.   (1)   The Contractor shall save harmless and indemnify the Employer from and against all claims and proceedings for or on account of infringement of any patent rights design trade-mark or name or other protected rights in respect of any Constructional Plant machine work or material used for or in connection with the Works and from and against all claims demands proceedings damages costs charges and expenses whatsoever in respect thereof or in relation thereto.

**Notices by Contractor to Employer**

(4)   The Contractor shall in relation to any part of the Works (other than Emergency Works) and subject to the compliance by the Employer with sub-clause (2) of this Clause give not less that 21 days notice in writing to the Employer before

(a)  commencing any part of the Works in a Street (as defined in Sections 1(3) and 38(1) of the Act) or

(b)  commencing any part of the Works in Controlled Land or in a Prospectively Maintainable Highway or

(c)  commencing in a Street or in Controlled Land or in a Prospectively Maintainable Highway any part of the Works which is likely to affect the apparatus of any Owning Undertaker (within the meaning of Section 26 of the Act).

Such notice shall state the date on which and the place at which the Contractor intends to commence the execution of the work referred to therein.

**Failure to commence Street Works**

(5)   If the Contractor having given any such notice as is required by sub-clause (4) of this Clause shall not commence the part of the Works to which such notice relates within 2 months after the date when such notice is given such notice shall be treated as invalid and compliance with the said sub-clause (4) shall be requisite as if such notice had not been given.

**Delays attributable to variations**

(6)   In the event of such a variation of the Works as is referred to in sub-clause (2)(b) of this Clause being ordered by or on behalf of the Employer and resulting in delay in the construction and completion of the Works by reason of the necessity of compliance by the Contractor with sub-clause (4) of this Clause the Engineer shall in addition to valuing the variation under Clause 52 take such delay into account in determining any extension of time to which the Contractor is entitled under Clause 44 and the Contractor shall subject to Clause 52(4) be paid in accordance with Clause 60 such additional cost as the Engineer shall consider to have been reasonably attributable to such delay.

**Contractor to comply with other obligations of Act**

(7)   Except as otherwise provided by this Clause where in relation to the carrying out of the Works the Act imposes any requirements or obligations upon the Employer the Contractor shall comply with such requirements and obligations and shall indemnify the Employer against any liability which the Employer may incur in consequence of any failure to comply with the said requirements and obligations.

**Patent rights**

**28** (1)   The Contractor shall save harmless and indemnify the Employer from and against all claims and proceedings for or on account of infringement of any patent right design trademark or name or other protected right in respect of any

(a)  Contractor's Equipment used for or in connection with the Works

(b)  materials plant and equipment for incorporation in the Works

and from and against all claims demands proceedings damages costs charges and expenses whatsoever in respect thereof or in relation thereto except where such infringement results from compliance with the design or Specification provided other than by the Contractor. In the latter event the Employer shall indemnify the Contractor from and against all claims and proceedings for or on account of infringement of any patent right design trademark or name or other protected right aforesaid.

**Royalties.**

(2)    Except where otherwise specified the Contractor shall pay all tonnage and other royalties rent and other payments or compensation (if any) for getting stone sand gravel clay or other materials required for the Works.

**Interference with Traffic and Adjoining Properties.**

**29.**    (1)    All operations necessary for the execution of the Works shall so far as compliance with the requirements of the Contract permits be carried on so as not to interfere unnecessarily or improperly with the public convenience or the access to or use or occupation of public or private roads and foot-paths or to or of properties whether in the possession of the Employer or of any other person and the Contractor shall save harmless and indemnify the Employer in respect of all claims demands proceedings damages costs charges and expenses whatsoever arising out of or in relation to any such matters.

**Noise and Disturbance.**

(2)    All work shall be carried out without unreasonable noise and disturbance.    The Contractor shall indemnify the Employer from and against any liability for damages on account of noise or other disturbance created while or in carrying out the work and from and against all claims demands proceedings damages costs charges and expenses whatsoever in regard or in relation to such liability.

**Avoidance of Damage to Highways, etc.**

**30.**    (1)    The Contractor shall use every reasonable means to prevent any of the highways or bridges communicating with or on the routes to the Site from being subjected to extraordinary traffic within the meaning of the Highways Act 1980 or in Scotland the Road Traffic Act 1930 or any statutory modification or re-enactment thereof by any traffic of the Contractor or any of his sub-contractors and in particular shall select routes and use vehicles and restrict and distribute loads so that any such extraordinary traffic as will inevitably arise from the moving of Constructional Plant and materials or manufactured or fabricated articles from and to the Site shall be limited as far as reasonably possible and so that no unnecessary damage or injury may be occasioned to such highways and bridges.

*This Clause has been extended to cover design and specification with an indemnity from the Employer in respect of any design or Specification provided other than by the Contractor.*

**Royalties**

(2)  Except where otherwise stated the Contractor shall pay all tonnage and other royalties rent and other payments or compensation (if any) for getting stone sand clay or other materials required for the Works.

**Interference with traffic and adjoining properties**

**29**  (1)  All operations necessary for the construction and completion of the Works shall so far as compliance with the requirements of the Contract permits be carried on so as not to interfere unnecessarily or improperly with

(a)  the convenience of the public, or

(b)  the access to public or private roads footpaths or properties whether in the possession of the Employer or of any other person and with the use or occupation thereof.

The Contractor shall save harmless and indemnify the Employer in respect of all claims demands proceedings damages costs charges and expenses whatsoever arising out of or in relation to any such matters.

**Noise disturbance and pollution**

(2)  All work shall be carried out without unreasonable noise or disturbance or other pollution.

**Indemnity by Contractor**

(3)  To the extent that noise disturbance or other pollution is not the unavoidable consequence of constructing and completing the Works or performing the Contract the Contractor shall indemnify the Employer from and against any liability for damages on that account and against all claims demands proceedings damages costs charges and expenses whatsoever in regard or in relation to such liability.

**Indemnity by Employer**

(4)  The Employer shall indemnify the Contractor from and against any liability for damages on account of noise disturbance or other pollution which is the unavoidable consequence of carrying out the Works and from and against all claims demands proceedings damages costs charges and expenses whatsoever in regard or in relation to such liability.

*Revised Clauses based on previous Clause 29(2) but extended to cover other pollution and with the reservation that if the noise disturbance and pollution is the unavoidable consequence of carrying out the work then the Contractor is indemnified by the Employer.*

**Avoidance of damage to highways etc.**

**30**  (1)  The Contractor shall use every reasonable means to prevent any of the highways or bridges communicating with or on the routes to the Site from being subjected to extraordinary traffic within the meaning of the Highways Act 1980 or in Scotland the Roads (Scotland) Act 1984 or any statutory modification or re-enactment thereof by any traffic of the Contractor or any of his sub-contractors and in particular shall select routes and use vehicles and restrict and distribute loads so that any such extraordinary traffic as will inevitably arise from the moving of Contractor's Equipment and materials or manufactured or fabricated articles from and to the Site shall be limited as far as reasonably possible and so that no unnecessary damage or injury may be occasioned to such highways and bridges.

**Transport of Constructional Plant.**

(2) Save insofar as the Contract otherwise provides the Contractor shall be responsible for and shall pay the cost of strengthening any bridges or altering or improving any highway communicating with the Site to facilitate the movement of Constructional Plant equipment or Temporary Works required in the execution of the Works and the Contractor shall indemnify and keep indemnified the Employer against all claims for damage to any highway or bridge communicating with the Site caused by such movement including such claims as may be made by any competent authority directly against the Employer pursuant to any Act of Parliament or other Statutory Instrument and shall negotiate and pay all claims arising solely out of such damage.

**Transport of Materials.**

(3) If notwithstanding sub-clause (1) of this Clause any damage shall occur to any bridge or highway communicating with the Site arising from the transport of materials or manufactured or fabricated articles in the execution of the Works the Contractor shall notify the Engineer as soon as he becomes aware of such damage or as soon as he receives any claim from the authority entitled to make such claim. Where under any Act of Parliament or other Statutory Instrument the haulier of such materials or manufactured or fabricated articles is required to indemnify the highway authority against damage the Employer shall not be liable for any costs charges or expenses in respect thereof or in relation thereto. In other cases the Employer shall negotiate the settlement of and pay all sums due in respect of such claim and shall indemnify the Contractor in respect thereof and in respect of all claims demands proceedings damages costs charges and expenses in relation thereto. Provided always that if and so far as any such claim or part thereof shall in the opinion of the Engineer be due to any failure on the part of the Contractor to observe and perform his obligations under sub-clause (1) of this Clause then the amount certified by the Engineer to be due to such failure shall be paid by the Contractor to the Employer or deducted from any sum due or which may become due to the Contractor.

**Facilities for Other Contractors.**

31. (1) The Contractor shall in accordance with the requirements of the Engineer afford all reasonable facilities for any other contractors employed by the Employer and their workmen and for the workmen of the Employer and of any other properly authorised authorities or statutory bodies who may be employed in the execution on or near the Site of any work not in the Contract or of any contract which the Employer may enter into in connection with or ancillary to the Works.

**Delay and Extra Cost.**

(2) If compliance with sub-clause (1) of this Clause shall involve the Contractor in delay or cost beyond that reasonably to be foreseen by an experienced contractor at the time of tender then the Engineer shall take such delay into account in determining any extension of time to which the Contractor is entitled under Clause 44 and the Contractor shall subject to Clause 52(4) be paid in accordance with Clause 60 the amount of such cost as may be reasonable.

**Transport of Contractor's Equipment**

(2) Save insofar as the Contract otherwise provides the Contractor shall be responsible for and shall pay the cost of strengthening any bridges or altering or improving any highway communicating with the Site to facilitate the movement of Contractor's Equipment or Temporary Works required in the execution of the Works and the Contractor shall indemnify and keep indemnified the Employer against all claims for damage to any highway or bridge communicating with the Site caused by such movement including such claims as may be made by any competent authority directly against the Employer pursuant to any Act of Parliament or other Statutory Instrument and shall negotiate and pay all claims arising solely out of such damage.

**Transport of materials**

(3) If notwithstanding sub-clause (1) of this Clause any damage shall occur to any bridge or highway communicating with the Site arising from the transport of materials or manufactured or fabricated articles in the execution of the Works the Contractor shall notify the Engineer as soon as he becomes aware of such damage or as soon as he receives any claim from the authority entitled to make such claim.

Where under any Act of Parliament or other Statutory Instrument the haulier of such materials or manufactured or fabricated articles is required to indemnify the highway authority against damage the Employer shall not be liable for any costs charges or expenses in respect thereof or in relation thereto.

In other cases the Employer shall negotiate the settlement of and pay all sums due in respect of such claim and shall indemnify the Contractor in respect thereof and in respect of all claims demands proceedings damages costs charges and expenses in relation thereto. Provided always that if and so far as any such claim or part thereof shall in the opinion of the Engineer be due to any failure on the part of the Contractor to observe and perform his obligations under sub-clause (1) of this Clause then the amount certified by the Engineer to be due to such failure shall be paid by the Contractor to the Employer or deducted from any sum due or which may become due to the Contractor.

**Facilities for other contractors**

**31** (1) The Contractor shall in accordance with the requirements of the Engineer or Engineer's Representative afford all reasonable facilities for any other contractors employed by the Employer and their workmen and for the workmen of the Employer and of any other properly authorised authorities or statutory bodies who may be employed in the execution on or near the Site of any work not in the Contract or of any contract which the Employer may enter into in connection with or ancillary to the Works.

*Clause extended to cover requirements of the Engineer's Representative.*

**Delay and extra cost**

(2) If compliance with sub-clause (1) of this Clause shall involve the Contractor in delay or cost beyond that reasonably to be foreseen by an experienced contractor at the time of tender then the Engineer shall take such delay into account in determining any extension of time to which the Contractor is entitled under Clause 44 and the Contractor shall subject to Clause 52(4) be paid in accordance with Clause 60 the amount of such cost as may be reasonable. Profit shall be added thereto in respect of any additional permanent or temporary work.

*Clause amended to indicate addition of profit to cost in respect of any additional permanent or temporary work.*

**Fossils, etc.**

**32.** All fossils coins articles of value or antiquity and structures or other remains or things of geological or archaeological interest discovered on the Site shall as between the Employer and the Contractor be deemed to be the absolute property of the Employer and the Contractor shall take reasonable precautions to prevent his workmen or any other persons from removing or damaging any such article or thing and shall immediately upon discovery thereof and before removal acquaint the Engineer of such discovery and carry out at the expense of the Employer the Engineer's orders as to the disposal of the same.

**Clearance of Site on Completion.**

**33.** On the completion of the Works the Contractor shall clear away and remove from the Site all Constructional Plant surplus material rubbish and Temporary Works of every kind and leave the whole of the Site and Permanent Works clean and in a workmanlike condition to the satisfaction of the Engineer.

## LABOUR

**Rates of Wages/Hours and Conditions of Operatives**

**34.** The Contractor shall in the execution of the Contract where appropriate pay rates of wages and observe the hours and conditions for the employment of operatives not less favourable than those established for the time being in the Working Rule Agreement of the Civil Engineering Construction Conciliation Board for Great Britian.

**Returns of Labour and Plant.**

**35.** The Contractor shall if required by the Engineer deliver to the Engineer or at his office a return in such form and at such intervals as the Engineer may prescribe showing in detail the numbers of the several classes of labour from time to time employed by the Contractor on the Site and such information respecting Constructional Plant as the Engineer may require. The Contractor shall require his sub-contractors to observe the provisions of this Clause.

## WORKMANSHIP AND MATERIALS

**Quality of Materials and Workmanship and Tests.**

**36.** (1) All materials and workmanship shall be of the respective kinds described in the Contract and in accordance with the Engineer's instructions and shall be subjected from time to time to such tests as the Engineer may direct at the place of manufacture or fabrication or on the Site or such other place or places as may be specified in the Contract. The Contractor shall provide such assistance instruments machines labour and materials as are normally required for examining measuring and testing any work and the quality weight or quantity of any materials used and shall supply samples of materials before incorporation in the Works for testing as may be selected and required by the Engineer.

**Cost of Samples.**

(2) All samples shall be supplied by the Contractor at his own cost if the supply thereof is clearly intended by or provided for in the Contract but if not then at the cost of the Employer.

**Cost of Tests.**

(3) The cost of making any test shall be borne by the Contractor if such test is clearly intended by or provided for in the Contract and (in the cases only of a test under load or of a test to ascertain whether the design of any finished or partially finished work is appropriate for the purposes which it was intended to fulfil) is particularised in the Specification or Bill of Quantities in sufficient detail to enable the Contractor to have priced or allowed for the same in his Tender. If any test is ordered by the Engineer which is either:—

    (a)   not so intended by or provided for; or

    (b)   (in the cases above mentioned) is not so particularised;

then the cost of such test shall be borne by the Contractor if the test shows the workmanship or materials not to be in accordance with the provisions of the Contract or the Engineer's instructions but otherwise by the Employer.

**Fossils etc.** **32** All fossils coins articles of value or antiquity and structures or other remains or things of geological or archaeological interest discovered on the Site shall as between the Employer and the Contractor be deemed to be the absolute property of the Employer and the Contractor shall take reasonable precautions to prevent his workmen or any other persons from removing or damaging any such article or thing and shall immediately upon discovery thereof and before removal acquaint the Engineer of such discovery and carry out at the expense of the Employer the Engineer's orders as to the disposal of the same.

**Clearance of Site on completion** **33** On the completion of the Works the Contractor shall clear away and remove from the Site all Contractor's Equipment surplus material rubbish and Temporary Works of every kind and leave the whole of the Site and Permanent Works clean and in a workmanlike condition to the satisfaction of the Engineer.

**34** (Not used)

*Previous Clause 34 not now required.*

**Returns of labour and Contractor's Equipment** **35** The Contractor shall if required by the Engineer deliver to the Engineer or the Engineer's Representative a return in such form and at such intervals as the Engineer may prescribe showing in detail the numbers of the several classes of labour from time to time employed by the Contractor on the Site and such information respecting Contractor's Equipment as the Engineer may require. The Contractor shall require his sub-contractors to observe the provisions of this Clause.

*This Clause now provides for returns required by the Engineer's Representative as well as by the Engineer.*

## WORKMANSHIP AND MATERIALS

**Quality of materials and workmanship and tests** **36** (1) All materials and workmanship shall be of the respective kinds described in the Contract and in accordance with the Engineer's instructions and shall be subjected from time to time to such tests as the Engineer may direct at the place of manufacture or fabrication or on the Site or such other place or places as may be specified in the Contract. The Contractor shall provide such assistance instruments machines labour and materials as are normally required for examining measuring and testing any work and the quality weight or quantity of any materials used and shall supply samples of materials before incorporation in the Works for testing as may be selected and required by the Engineer.

**Cost of samples** (2) All samples shall be supplied by the Contractor at his own cost if the supply thereof is clearly intended by or provided for in the Contract but if not then at the cost of the Employer.

**Cost of tests** (3) The cost of making any test shall be borne by the Contractor if such test is clearly intended by or provided for in the Contract and (in the cases only of a test under load or of a test to ascertain whether the design of any finished or partially finished work is appropriate for the purposes which it was intended to fulfil) is particularized in the Specification or Bill of Quantities in sufficient detail to enable the Contractor to have priced or allowed for the same in his Tender. If any test is ordered by the Engineer which is either

(a) not so intended by or provided for or

(b) (in the cases above mentioned) is not so particularized

59

**Access to Site.** 37. The Engineer and any person authorised by him shall at all times have access to the Works and to the Site and to all workshops and places where work is being prepared or whence materials manufactured articles and machinery are being obtained for the Works and the Contractor shall afford every facility for and every assistance in or in obtaining the right to such access.

**Examination of Work before Covering up.** 38. (1) No work shall be covered up or put out of view without the approval of the Engineer and the Contractor shall afford full opportunity for the Engineer to examine and measure any work which is about to be covered up or put out of view and to examine foundations before permanent work is placed thereon. The Contractor shall give due notice to the Engineer whenever any such work or foundations is or are ready or about to be ready for examination and the Engineer shall without unreasonable delay unless he considers it unnecessary and advises the Contractor accordingly attend for the purpose of examining and measuring such work or of examining such foundations.

**Uncovering and Making Openings.** (2) The Contractor shall uncover any part or parts of the Works or make openings in or through the same as the Engineer may from time to time direct and shall reinstate and make good such part or parts to the satisfaction of the Engineer. If any such part or parts have been covered up or put out of view after compliance with the requirements of sub-clause (1) of this Clause and are found to be executed in accordance with the Contract the cost of uncovering making openings in or through reinstating and making good the same shall be borne by the Employer but in any other case all such cost shall be borne by the Contractor.

**Removal of Improper Work and Materials.** 39. (1) The Engineer shall during the progress of the Works have power to order in writing:—

    (a) the removal from the Site within such time or times as may be specified in the order of any materials which in the opinion of the Engineer are not in accordance with the Contract;

    (b) the substitution of proper and suitable materials; and

    (c) the removal and proper re-execution (notwithstanding any previous test thereof or interim payment therefor) of any work which in respect of materials or workmanship is not in the opinion of the Engineer in accordance with the Contract.

**Default of Contractor in Compliance.** (2) In case of default on the part of the Contractor in carrying out such order the Employer shall be entitled to employ and pay other persons to carry out the same and all expenses consequent thereon or incidental thereto shall be borne by the Contractor and shall be recoverable from him by the Employer or may be deducted by the Employer from any monies due or which may become due to the Contractor.

then the cost of such test shall be borne by the Contractor if the test shows the workmanship or materials not to be in accordance with the provisions of the Contract or the Engineer's instructions but otherwise by the Employer.

**Access to Site** 37 The Engineer and any person authorized by him shall at all times have access to the Works and to the Site and to all workshops and places where work is being prepared or whence materials manufactured articles and machinery are being obtained for the Works and the Contractor shall afford every facility for and every assistance in obtaining such access or the right to such access.

**Examination of work before covering up** 38 (1) No work shall be covered up or put out of view without the consent of the Engineer and the Contractor shall afford full opportunity for the Engineer to examine and measure any work which is about to be covered up or put out of view and to examine foundations before permanent work is placed thereon. The Contractor shall give due notice to the Engineer whenever any such work or foundations is or are ready or about to be ready for examination and the Engineer shall without unreasonable delay unless he considers it unnecessary and advises the Contractor accordingly attend for the purpose of examining and measuring such work or of examining such foundations.

**Uncovering and making openings** (2) The Contractor shall uncover any part or parts of the Works or make openings in or through the same as the Engineer may from time to time direct and shall reinstate and make good such part or parts to the satisfaction of the Engineer. If any such part or parts have been covered up or put out of view after compliance with the requirements of sub-clause (1) of this Clause and are found to be executed in accordance with the Contract the cost of uncovering making openings in or through reinstating and making good the same shall be borne by the Employer but in any other case all such cost shall be borne by the Contractor.

**Removal of unsatisfactory work and materials** 39 (1) The Engineer shall during the progress of the Works have power to instruct in writing the

(a) removal from the Site within such time or times specified in the instruction of any materials which in the opinion of the Engineer are not in accordance with the Contract

(b) substitution with materials in accordance with the Contract and

(c) removal and proper re-execution notwithstanding any previous test thereof or interim payment therefor of any work which in respect of

(i) material or workmanship or

(ii) design by the Contractor or for which he is responsible

is not in the opinion of the Engineer in accordance with the Contract.

**Default of Contractor in compliance** (2) In case of default on the part of the Contractor in carrying out such instruction the Employer shall be entitled to employ and pay other persons to carry out the same and all costs consequent thereon or incidental thereto as determined by the Engineer shall be recoverable from the Contractor by the Employer and may be deducted by the Employer from any monies due or to become due to him and the Engineer shall notify the Contractor accordingly with a copy to the Employer.

61

**Failure to Disapprove.**

(3) Failure of the Engineer or any person acting under him pursuant to Clause 2 to disapprove any work or materials shall not prejudice the power of the Engineer or any of them subsequently to disapprove such work or materials.

**Suspension of Work.**

40. (1) The Contractor shall on the written order of the Engineer suspend the progress of the Works or any part thereof for such time or times and in such manner as the Engineer may consider necessary and shall during such suspension properly protect and secure the work so far as is necessary in the opinion of the Engineer. Subject to Clause 52(4) the Contractor shall be paid in accordance with Clause 60 the extra cost (if any) incurred in giving effect to the Engineer's instructions under this Clause except to the extent that such suspension is:—

    (a) otherwise provided for in the Contract; or

    (b) necessary by reason of weather conditions or by some default on the part of the Contractor; or

    (c) necessary for the proper execution of the work or for the safety of the Works or any part thereof inasmuch as such necessity does not arise from any act or default of the Engineer or the Employer or from any of the Excepted Risks defined in Clause 20.

The Engineer shall take any delay occasioned by a suspension ordered under this Clause (including that arising from any act or default of the Engineer or the Employer) into account in determining any extension of time to which the Contractor is entitled under Clause 44 except when such suspension is otherwise provided for in the Contract or is necessary by reason of some default on the part of the Contractor.

**Suspension lasting more than Three Months.**

(2) If the progress of the Works or any part thereof is suspended on the written order of the Engineer and if permission to resume work is not given by the Engineer within a period of 3 months from the date of suspension then the Contractor may unless such suspension is otherwise provided for in the Contract or continues to be necessary by reason of some default on the part of the Contractor serve a written notice on the Engineer requiring permission within 28 days from the receipt of such notice to proceed with the Works or that part thereof in regard to which progress is suspended. If within the said 28 days the Engineer does not grant such permission the Contractor by a further written notice so served may (but is not bound to) elect to treat the suspension where it affects part only of the Works as an omission of such part under Clause 51 or where it affects the whole Works as an abandonment of the Contract by the Employer.

## COMMENCEMENT TIME AND DELAYS

**Commencement of Works.**

41. The Contractor shall commence the Works on or as soon as is reasonably possible after the Date for Commencement of the Works to be notified by the Engineer in writing which date shall be within a reasonable time after the date of acceptance of the Tender. Thereafter the Contractor shall proceed with the Works with due expedition and without delay in accordance with the Contract.

**Failure to disapprove**

(3)   Failure of the Engineer or any person acting under him pursuant to Clause 2 to disapprove any work or materials shall not prejudice the power of the Engineer or any such person subsequently to take action under this Clause.

**Suspension of work**

**40**   (1)   The Contractor shall on the written order of the Engineer suspend the progress of the Works or any part thereof for such time or times and in such manner as the Engineer may consider necessary and shall during such suspension properly protect and secure the work so far as is necessary in the opinion of the Engineer. Subject to Clause 52(4) the Contractor shall be paid in accordance with Clause 60 the extra cost (if any) incurred in giving effect to the Engineer's instructions under this Clause except to the extent that such suspension is

    (a)   otherwise provided for in the Contract or

    (b)   necessary by reason of weather conditions or by some default on the part of the Contractor or

    (c)   necessary for the proper execution or for the safety of the Works or any part thereof in as much as such necessity does not arise from any act or default of the Engineer or the Employer or from any of the Excepted Risks defined in Clause 20(2).

Profit shall be added thereto in respect of any additional permanent or temporary work.

The Engineer shall take any delay occasioned by a suspension ordered under this Clause (including that arising from any act or default of the Engineer or the Employer) into account in determining any extension of time to which the Contractor is entitled under Clause 44 except when such suspension is otherwise provided for in the Contract or is necessary by reason of some default on the part of the Contractor.

*Clause amended to indicate addition of profit to cost in respect of any additional permanent or temporary work.*

**Suspension lasting more than three months**

(2)   If the progress of the Works or any part thereof is suspended on the written order of the Engineer and if permission to resume work is not given by the Engineer within a period of 3 months from the date of suspension then the Contractor may unless such suspension is otherwise provided for in the Contract or continues to be necessary by reason of some default on the part of the Contractor serve a written notice on the Engineer requiring permission within 28 days from the receipt of such notice to proceed with the Works or that part thereof in regard to which progress is suspended. If within the said 28 days the Engineer does not grant such permission the Contractor by a further written notice so served may (but is not bound to) elect to treat the suspension where it affects part only of the Works as an omission of such part under Clause 51 or where it affects the whole Works as an abandonment of the Contract by the Employer.

## COMMENCEMENT TIME AND DELAYS

**Works Commencement Date**

**41**   (1)   The Works Commencement Date shall be

    (a)   the date specified in the Appendix to the Form of Tender or if no date is specified

    (b)   a date within 28 days of the award of the Contract to be notified by the Engineer in writing or

    (c)   such other date as may be agreed between the parties.

**Possession of Site.**

**42.** (1)   Save in so far as the Contract may prescribe the extent of portions of the Site of which the Contractor is to be given possession from time to time and the order in which such portions shall be made available to him and subject to any requirement in the Contract as to the order in which the Works shall be executed the Employer will at the Date for Commencement of the Works notified under Clause 41 give to the Contractor possession of so much of the Site as may be required to enable the Contractor to commence and proceed with the construction of the Works in accordance with the programme referred to in Clause 14 and will from time to time as the Works proceed give to the Contractor possession of such further portions of the Site as may be required to enable the Contractor to proceed with the construction of the Works with due despatch in accordance with the said programme.   If the Contractor suffers delay or incurs cost from failure on the part of the Employer to give possession in accordance with the terms of this Clause then the Engineer shall take such delay into account in determining any extension of time to which the Contractor is entitled under Clause 44 and the Contractor shall subject to Clause 52(4) be paid in accordance with Clause 60 the amount of such cost as may be reasonable.

**Wayleaves, etc.**

(2)   The Contractor shall bear all expenses and charges for special or temporary wayleaves required by him in connection with access to the Site.   The Contractor shall also provide at his own cost any additional accommodation outside the Site required by him for the purposes of the Works.

*New Clause to identify clearly the date of commencement of the Contract as distinct from the date work actually starts.*

**Start of Works**

(2)   The Contractor shall start the Works on or as soon as is reasonably practicable after the Works Commencement Date. Thereafter the Contractor shall proceed with the Works with due expedition and without delay in accordance with the Contract.

*This Clause covers the remainder of previous Clause 41.*

**Possession of Site and access**

**42**   (1)   The Contract may prescribe

(a)   the extent of portions of the Site of which the Contractor is to be given possession from time to time

(b)   the order in which such portions of the Site shall be made available to the Contractor

(c)   the availability and the nature of the access which is to be provided by the Employer

(d)   the order in which the Works shall be constructed.

*Substantially as the first four lines of previous Clause 42(1) but rearranged. An additional requirement has been added in respect of access to the Site.*

(2)   (a)   Subject to sub-clause (1) of this Clause the Employer shall give to the Contractor on the Works Commencement Date possession of so much of the Site and access thereto as may be required to enable the Contractor to commence and proceed with the construction of the Works.

(b)   Thereafter the Employer shall during the course of the Works give to the Contractor possession of such further portions of the Site as may be required in accordance with the programme which the Engineer has accepted under Clause 14 and such further access as is necessary to enable the Contractor to proceed with the construction of the Works with due despatch.

*Substantially as previous Clause 42(1) lines 4-10 but with reference to access added. The Clause is subdivided into (a) and (b) covering the initial requirements at the start of the Contract and the further requirements.*

**Failure to give possession**

(3)   If the Contractor suffers delay and/or incurs additional cost from failure on the part of the Employer to give possession in accordance with the terms of this Clause the Engineer shall determine

(a)   any extension of time to which the Contractor is entitled under Clause 44 and

(b)   subject to Clause 52(4) the amount of any additional cost to which the Contractor may be entitled. Profit shall be added thereto in respect of any additional permanent or temporary work.

The Engineer shall notify the Contractor accordingly with a copy to the Employer.

*Clause amended to indicate addition of profit to cost in respect of any additional permanent or temporary work.*

**Access and facilities provided by the Contractor**

(4)   The Contractor shall bear all costs and charges for any access required by him additional to those provided by the Employer. The Contractor shall also provide at his own cost any additional facilities outside the Site required by him for the purposes of the Works.

**Time for Completion.**

**43.** The whole of the Works and any Section required to be completed within a particular time as stated in the Appendix to the Form of Tender shall be completed within the time so stated (or such extended time as may be allowed under Clause 44) calculated from the Date for Commencement of the Works notified under Clause 41.

**Extension of Time for Completion.**

**44.** (1) Should any variation ordered under Clause 51(1) or increased quantities referred to in Clause 51(3) or any other cause of delay referred to in these Conditions or exceptional adverse weather conditions or other special circumstances of any kind whatsoever which may occur be such as fairly to entitle the Contractor to an extension of time for the completion of the Works or (where different periods for completion of different Sections are provided for in the Appendix to the Form of Tender) of the relevant Section the Contractor shall within 28 days after the cause of the delay has arisen or as soon thereafter as is reasonable in all the circumstances deliver to the Engineer full and detailed particulars of any claim to extension of time to which he may consider himself entitled in order that such claim may be investigated at the time.

**Interim Assessment of Extension.**

(2) The Engineer shall upon receipt of such particulars or if he thinks fit in the absence of any such claim consider all the circumstances known to him at that time and make an assessment of the extension of time (if any) to which he considers the Contractor entitled for the completion of the Works or relevant Section and shall by notice in writing to the Contractor grant such extension of time for completion. In the event that the Contractor shall have made a claim for an extension of time but the Engineer considers the Contractor not entitled thereto the Engineer shall so inform the Contractor.

**Assessment at Due Date for Completion.**

(3) The Engineer shall at or as soon as possible after the due date or extended date for completion (and whether or not the Contractor shall have made any claim for an extension of time) consider all the circumstances known to him at that time and take action similar to that provided for in sub-clause (2) of this Clause. Should the Engineer consider that the Contractor is not entitled to an extension of time he shall so notify the Employer and the Contractor.

**Time for completion**    **43**    The whole of the Works and any Section required to be completed within a particular time as stated in the Appendix to the Form of Tender shall be substantially completed within the time so stated (or such extended time as may be allowed under Clause 44) calculated from the Works Commencement Date.

**Extension of time for completion**    **44**    (1)    Should the Contractor consider that

(a)    any variation ordered under Clause 51(1) or

(b)    increased quantities referred to in Clause 51(4) or

(c)    any cause of delay referred to in these Conditions or

(d)    exceptional adverse weather conditions or

(e)    other special circumstances of any kind whatsoever which may occur

be such as to entitle him to an extension of time for the substantial completion of the Works or any Section thereof he shall within 28 days after the cause of any delay has arisen or as soon thereafter as is reasonable deliver to the Engineer full and detailed particulars in justification of the period of extension claimed in order that the claim may be investigated at the time.

**Assessment of delay**    (2)    (a)    The Engineer shall upon receipt of such particulars consider all the circumstances known to him at that time and make an assessment of the delay (if any) that has been suffered by the Contractor as a result of the alleged cause and shall so notify the Contractor in writing.

(b) The Engineer may in the absence of any claim make an assessment of the delay that he considers has been suffered by the Contractor as a result of any of the circumstances listed in sub-clause (1) of this Clause and shall so notify the Contractor in writing.

*New Clause providing in the first instance for an assessment by the Engineer of the delay suffered with due notification thereof to the Contractor in writing.*

**Interim grant of extension of time**    (3)    Should the Engineer consider that the delay suffered fairly entitles the Contractor to an extension of the time for the substantial completion of the Works or any Section thereof such interim extension shall be granted forthwith and be notified to the Contractor in writing. In the event that the Contractor has made a claim for an extension of time but the Engineer does not consider the Contractor entitled to an extension of time he shall so inform the Contractor without delay.

*New provision under which an extension of time is to be given but only if in the opinion of the Engineer it will actually be required for the completion of the Works (or a Section thereof).*

**Assessment at due date for completion**    (4)    The Engineer shall not later than 14 days after the due date or extended date for completion of the Works or any Section thereof (and whether or not the Contractor shall have made any claim for an extension of time) consider all the circumstances known to him at that time and take action similar to that provided for in sub-clause (3) of this Clause. Should the Engineer consider that the Contractor is not entitled to an extension of time he shall so notify the Employer and the Contractor.

*Substantially as previous Clause 44(3) but with a time limit of 14 days imposed.*

**Final Determination of Extension.**

(4) The Engineer shall upon the issue of the Certificate of Completion of the Works or of the relevant Section review all the circumstances of the kind referred to in sub-clause (1) of this Clause and shall finally determine and certify to the Contractor the overall extension of time (if any) to which he considers the Contractor entitled in respect of the Works or any relevant Section. No such final review of the circumstances shall result in a decrease in any extension of time already granted by the Engineer pursuant to sub-clauses (2) or (3) of this Clause.

**Night and Sunday Work.**

45. Subject to any provision to the contrary contained in the Contract none of the Works shall be executed during the night or on Sundays without the permission in writing of the Engineer save when the work is unavoidable or absolutely necessary for the saving of life or property or for the safety of the Works in which case the Contractor shall immediately advise the Engineer or the Engineer's Representative. Provided always that this Clause shall not be applicable in the case of any work which it is customary to carry out outside normal working hours or by rotary or double shifts.

**Rate of Progress.**

46. If for any reason which does not entitle the Contractor to an extension of time the rate of progress of the Works or any Section is at any time in the opinion of the Engineer too slow to ensure completion by the prescribed time or extended time for completion the Engineer shall so notify the Contractor in writing and the Contractor shall thereupon take such steps as are necessary and the Engineer may approve to expedite progress so as to complete the Works or such Section by the prescribed time or extended time. The Contractor shall not be entitled to any additional payment for taking such steps. If as a result of any notice given by the Engineer under this Clause the Contractor shall seek the Engineer's permission to do any work at night or on Sundays such permission shall not be unreasonably refused.

**Final determination of extension**

(5)   The Engineer shall within 14 days of the issue of the Certificate of Substantial Completion for the Works or for any Section thereof review all the circumstances of the kind referred to in sub-clause (1) of this Clause and shall finally determine and certify to the Contractor with a copy to the Employer the overall extension of time (if any) to which he considers the Contractor entitled in respect of the Works or the relevant Section. No such final review of the circumstances shall result in a decrease in any extension of time already granted by the Engineer pursuant to sub-clauses (3) or (4) of this Clause.

*Substantially as previous Clause 44(4) but with a time limit of 14 days imposed.*

**Night and Sunday work**

45   Subject to any provision to the contrary contained in the Contract none of the Works shall be executed during the night or on Sundays without the permission in writing of the Engineer save when the work is unavoidable or absolutely necessary for the saving of life or property or for the safety of the Works in which case the Contractor shall immediately advise the Engineer or the Engineer's Representative. Provided always that this Clause shall not be applicable in the case of any work which it is customary to carry out outside normal working hours or by rotary or double shifts.

**Rate of progress**

46   (1)   If for any reason which does not entitle the Contractor to an extension of time the rate of progress of the Works or any Section is at any time in the opinion of the Engineer too slow to ensure substantial completion by the time or extended time for completion prescribed by Clause 43 and 44 as appropriate the Engineer shall notify the Contractor in writing and the Contractor shall thereupon take such steps as are necessary and to which the Engineer may consent to expedite the progress so as substantially to complete the Works or such Section by that prescribed time or extended time. The Contractor shall not be entitled to any additional payment for taking such steps.

**Permission to work at night or on Sundays**

(2)   If as a result of any notice given by the Engineer under sub-clause (1) of this Clause the Contractor shall seek the Engineer's permission to do any work on Site at night or on Sundays such permission shall not be unreasonably refused.

*Substantially as previous Clause 46 lines 7-9 but it is made clear that the requirement for permission to work at night or on Sundays only applies to work on Site.*

**Provision for accelerated completion**

(3)   If the Contractor is requested by the Employer or the Engineer to complete the Works or any Section within a revised time being less than the time or extended time for completion prescribed by Clauses 43 and 44 as appropriate and the Contractor agrees so to do then any special terms and conditions of payment shall be agreed between the Contractor and the Employer before any such action is taken.

*New Clause providing for earlier completion if special terms and conditions of payment can be agreed.*

69

# LIQUIDATED DAMAGES AND LIMITATION OF DAMAGES FOR DELAYED COMPLETION

**Liquidated Damages for Whole of Works.**

**47.** (1) (a) In the Appendix to the Form of Tender under the heading " Liquidated Damages for Delay " there is stated in column 1 the sum which represents the Employer's genuine pre-estimate (expressed as a rate per week or per day as the case may be) of the damages likely to be suffered by him in the event that the whole of the Works shall not be completed within the time prescribed by Clause 43.

Provided that in lieu of such sum there may be stated such lesser sum as represents the limit of the Contractor's liability for damages for failure to complete the whole of the Works within the time for completion therefor or any extension thereof granted under Clause 44.

(b) If the Contractor should fail to complete the whole of the Works within the prescribed time or any extension thereof granted under Clause 44 the Contractor shall pay to the Employer for such default the sum stated in column 1 aforesaid for every week or day as the case may be which shall elapse between the date on which the prescribed time or any extension thereof expired and the date of completion of the whole of the Works. Provided that if any part of the Works not being a Section or part of a Section shall be certified as complete pursuant to Clause 48 before completion of the whole of the Works the sum stated in column 1 shall be reduced by the proportion which the value of the part completed bears to the value of the whole of the Works.

**Liquidated Damages for Sections.**

(2) (a) In cases where any Section shall be required to be completed within a particular time as stated in the Appendix to the Form of Tender there shall also be stated in the said Appendix under the heading " Liquidated Damages for Delay " in column 2 the sum by which the damages stated in column 1 or the limit of the Contractor's said liability as the case may be shall be reduced upon completion of each such Section and in column 3 the sum which represents the Employer's genuine pre-estimate (expressed as aforesaid) of any specific damage likely to be suffered by him in the event that such Section shall not be completed within that time.

Provided that there may be stated in column 3 in lieu of such sum such lesser sum as represents the limit of the Contractor's liability for failure to complete the relevant Section within the relevant time.

(b) If the Contractor should fail to complete any Section within the relevant time for completion or any extension thereof granted under Clause 44 the Contractor shall pay to the Employer for such default the sum stated in column 3 aforesaid for every week or day as the case may be which shall elapse between the date on which the relevant time or any extension thereof expired and the date of completion of the relevant Section. Provided that:—

(i) if completion of a Section shall be delayed beyond the due date for completion of the whole of the Works the damages payable under sub-clauses (1) and (2) of this Clause until completion of that Section shall be the sum stated in column 1 plus in respect of that Section the sum stated in column 3 less the sum stated in column 2;

(ii) if any part of a Section shall be certified as complete pursuant to Clause 48 before completion of the whole thereof the sums stated in columns 2 and 3 in respect of that Section shall be reduced by the proportion which the value of the part bears to the value of the Section and the sum stated in column 1 shall be reduced by the same amount as the sum in column 2 is reduced; and

(iii) upon completion of any such Section the sum stated in column 1 shall be reduced by the sum stated in column 2 in respect of that Section at the date of such completion.

**Damages not a Penalty.**

(3) All sums payable by the Contractor to the Employer pursuant to this Clause shall be paid as liquidated damages for delay and not as a penalty.

# LIQUIDATED DAMAGES FOR DELAY

*Clause 47 has been substantially revised to separate the different situations that can exist, first when dealing with the whole of the Works and second when the Works is divided into Sections. Provision is made as previously for the reduction of the liquidated damages should part of the Works or part of a Section of the Works have been certified as complete. Provision has now been made for a limit to be placed on liquidated damages if so desired (Clause 47(4)(a)) and it is made clear that where no sum for liquidated damages is quoted in the Appendix to the Form of Tender then no damages will be payable (Clause 47(4)(b)). Note that Clause 47(1) or 47(2) can apply as appropriate but not both.*

**Liquidated damages for delay in substantial completion of the whole of the Works**

**47** (1) (a) Where the whole of the Works is not divided into Sections the Appendix to the Form of Tender shall include a sum which represents the Employer's genuine pre-estimate (expressed per week or per day as the case may be) of the damages likely to be suffered by him if the whole of the Works is not substantially completed within the time prescribed by Clause 43 or by any extension thereof granted under Clause 44 or by any revision thereof agreed under Clause 46(3) as the case may be.

(b) If the Contractor fails to complete the whole of the Works within the time so prescribed he shall pay to the Employer the said sum for every week or day (as the case may be) which shall elapse between the date on which the prescribed time expired and the date the whole of the Works is substantially completed.

Provided that if any part of the Works is certified as complete pursuant to Clause 48 before the completion of the whole of the Works the said sum shall be reduced by the proportion which the value of the part so completed bears to the value of the whole of the Works.

**Liquidated damages for delay in substantial completion where the whole of the Works is divided into Sections**

(2) (a) Where the Works is divided into Sections (together comprising the whole of the Works) which are required to be completed within particular times as stated in the Appendix to the Form of Tender sub-clause (1) of this Clause shall not apply and the said Appendix shall include a sum in respect of each Section which represents the Employer's genuine pre-estimate (expressed per week or per day as the case may be) of the damages likely to be suffered by him if that Section is not substantially completed within the time prescribed by Clause 43 or by any extension thereof granted under Clause 44 or by any revision thereof agreed under Clause 46(3) as the case may be.

(b) If the Contractor fails to complete any Section within the time so prescribed he shall pay to the Employer the appropriate stated sum for every week or day (as the case may be) which shall elapse between the date on which the prescribed time expired and the date of substantial completion of that Section.

Provided that if any part of that Section is certified as complete pursuant to Clause 48 before the completion of the whole thereof the appropriate stated sum shall be reduced by the proportion which the value of the part so completed bears to the value of the whole of that Section.

(c) Liquidated damages in respect of two or more Sections may where circumstances so dictate run concurrently.

**Damages not a penalty**

(3) All sums payable by the Contractor to the Employer pursuant to this Clause shall be paid as liquidated damages for delay and not as a penalty.

**Deduction of Liquidated Damages.**

(4) If the Engineer shall under Clause 44 (3) or (4) have determined and certified any extension of time to which he considers the Contractor entitled or shall have notified the Employer and the Contractor that he is of the opinion that the Contractor is not entitled to any or any further extension of time the Employer may deduct and retain from any sum otherwise payable by the Employer to the Contractor hereunder the amount which in the event that the Engineer's said opinion should not be subsequently revised would be the amount of the liquidated damages payable by the Contractor under this Clause.

**Reimbursement of Liquidated Damages.**

(5) If upon a subsequent or final review of the circumstances causing delay the Engineer shall grant an extension or further extension of time or if an arbitrator appointed under Clause 66 shall decide that the Engineer should have granted such an extension or further extension of time the Employer shall no longer be entitled to liquidated damages in respect of the period of such extension of time. Any sums in respect of such period which may have been recovered pursuant to sub-clause (3) of this Clause shall be reimbursable forthwith to the Contractor together with interest at the rate provided for in Clause 60(6) from the date on which such liquidated damages were recovered from the Contractor.

**Limitation of liquidated damages**

(4) (a) The total amount of liquidated damages in respect of the whole of the Works or any Section thereof shall be limited to the appropriate sum stated in the Appendix to the Form of Tender. If no such limit is stated therein then liquidated damages without limit shall apply.

(b) Should there be omitted from the Appendix to the Form of Tender any sum required to be inserted therein either by sub-clause (1)(a) or by sub-clause (2)(a) of this Clause as the case may be or if any such sum is stated to be "nil" then to that extent damages shall not be payable.

**Recovery and reimbursement of liquidated damages**

(5) The Employer may

(a) deduct and retain the amount of any liquidated damages becoming due under the provision of this Clause from any sums due or which become due to the Contractor or

(b) require the Contractor to pay such amount to the Employer forthwith.

If upon a subsequent or final review of the circumstances causing delay the Engineer grants a relevant extension or further extension of time the Employer shall no longer be entitled to liquidated damages in respect of the period of such extension.

Any sum in respect of such period which may already have been recovered under this Clause shall be reimbursed forthwith to the Contractor together with interest at the rate provided for in Clause 60(7) from the date on which such sums were recovered from the Contractor.

**Intervention of variations etc.**

(6) If after liquidated damages have become payable in respect of any part of the Works the Engineer issues a variation order under Clause 51 or adverse physical conditions or artificial obstructions within the meaning of Clause 12 are encountered or any other situation outside the Contractor's control arises any of which in the Engineer's opinion results in further delay to that part of the Works

(a) the Engineer shall so inform the Contractor and the Employer in writing and

(b) the Employer's entitlement to liquidated damages in respect of that part of the Works shall be suspended until the Engineer notifies the Contractor and the Employer in writing that the further delay has come to an end.

Such suspension shall not invalidate any entitlement to liquidated damages which accrued before the period of delay started to run and any monies deducted or paid in accordance with sub-clause (5) of this Clause may be retained by the Employer without incurring liability for interest thereon under Clause 60(7).

*Clause 47(6) outlines the procedure that has to follow the issue of a variation order or the acceptance of a Clause 12 situation that affects the liquidated damages that had become payable.*

## COMPLETION CERTIFICATE

**Certificate of Completion of Works.**

**48.** (1) When the Contractor shall consider that the whole of the Works has been substantially completed and has satisfactorily passed any final test that may be prescribed by the Contract he may give a notice to that effect to the Engineer or to the Engineer's Representative accompanied by an undertaking to finish any outstanding work during the Period of Maintenance. Such notice and undertaking shall be in writing and shall be deemed to be a request by the Contractor for the Engineer to issue a Certificate of Completion in respect of the Works and the Engineer shall within 21 days of the date of delivery of such notice either issue to the Contractor (with a copy to the Employer) a Certificate of Completion stating the date on which in his opinion the Works were substantially completed in accordance with the Contract or else give instructions in writing to the Contractor specifying all the work which in the Engineer's opinion requires to be done by the Contractor before the issue of such certificate. If the Engineer shall give such instructions the Contractor shall be entitled to receive such Certificate of Completion within 21 days of completion to the satisfaction of the Engineer of the work specified by the said instructions.

**Completion of Sections and Occupied Parts.**

(2) Similarly in accordance with the procedure set out in sub-clause (1) of this Clause the Contractor may request and the Engineer shall issue a Certificate of Completion in respect of:—

    (a) any Section in respect of which a separate time for completion is provided in the Appendix to the Form of Tender; and

    (b) any substantial part of the Works which has been both completed to the satisfaction of the Engineer and occupied or used by the Employer.

**Completion of Other Parts of Works.**

(3) If the Engineer shall be of the opinion that any part of the Works shall have been substantially completed and shall have satisfactorily passed any final test that may be prescribed by the Contract he may issue a Certificate of Completion in respect of that part of the Works before completion of the whole of the Works and upon the issue of such certificate the Contractor shall be deemed to have undertaken to complete any outstanding work in that part of the Works during the Period of Maintenance.

**Reinstatement of Ground.**

(4) Provided always that a Certificate of Completion given in respect of any Section or part of the Works before completion of the whole shall not be deemed to certify completion of any ground or surfaces requiring reinstatement unless such certificate shall expressly so state.

# CERTIFICATE OF SUBSTANTIAL COMPLETION

**Notification of substantial completion**

**48** (1) When the Contractor considers that

    (a) the whole of the Works or

    (b) any Section in respect of which a separate time for completion is provided in the Appendix to the Form of Tender

has been substantially completed and has satisfactorily passed any final test that may be prescribed by the Contract he may give notice in writing to that effect to the Engineer or to the Engineer's Representative. Such notice shall be accompanied by an undertaking to finish any outstanding work in accordance with the provisions of Clause 49(1).

**Certification of substantial completion**

(2) The Engineer shall within 21 days of the date of delivery of such notice either

    (a) issue to the Contractor (with a copy to the Employer) a Certificate of Substantial Completion stating the date on which in his opinion the Works were or the Section was substantially completed in accordance with the Contract or

    (b) give instructions in writing to the Contractor specifying all the work which in the Engineer's opinion requires to be done by the Contractor before the issue of such certificate.

If the Engineer gives such instructions the Contractor shall be entitled to receive a Certificate of Substantial Completion within 21 days of completion to the satisfaction of the Engineer of the work specified in the said instructions.

**Premature use by Employer**

(3) If any substantial part of the Works has been occupied or used by the Employer other than as provided in the Contract the Contractor may request in writing and the Engineer shall issue a Certificate of Substantial Completion in respect thereof. Such certificate shall take effect from the date of delivery of the Contractor's request and upon the issue of such certificate the Contractor shall be deemed to have undertaken to complete any outstanding work in that part of the Works during the Defects Correction Period.

*This Clause conveys the right that was in previous Clause 48(2)(b) for the Contractor to receive a Certificate of Substantial Completion in respect of any substantial part of the Works that has been occupied and used by the Employer (other than as provided for in the Contract).*

**Substantial completion of other parts of the Works**

(4) If the Engineer considers that any part of the Works has been substantially completed and has passed any final test that may be prescribed by the Contract he may issue a Certificate of Substantial Completion in respect of that part of the Works before completion of the whole of the Works and upon the issue of such certificate the Contractor shall be deemed to have undertaken to complete any outstanding work in that part of the Works during the Defects Correction Period.

**Reinstatement of ground**

(5) A Certificate of Substantial Completion given in respect of any Section or part of the Works before completion of the whole shall not be deemed to certify completion of any ground or surfaces requiring reinstatement unless such certificate shall expressly so state.

**Definition of " Period of Maintenance ".**

**49.** (1) In these Conditions the expression " Period of Maintenance " shall mean the period of maintenance named in the Appendix to the Form of Tender calculated from the date of completion of the Works or any Section or part thereof certified by the Engineer in accordance with Clause 48 as the case may be.

**Execution of Work of Repair, etc.**

(2) To the intent that the Works and each Section and part thereof shall at or as soon as practicable after the expiration of the relevant Period of Maintenance be delivered up to the Employer in the condition required by the Contract (fair wear and tear excepted) to the satisfaction of the Engineer the Contractor shall finish the work (if any) outstanding at the date of completion as certified under Clause 48 as soon as may be practicable after such date and shall execute all such work of repair amendment reconstruction rectification and making good of defects imperfections shrinkages or other faults as may during the Period of Maintenance or within 14 days after its expiration be required of the Contractor in writing by the Engineer as a result of an inspection made by or on behalf of the Engineer prior to its expiration.

**Cost of Execution of Work of Repair, etc.**

(3) All such work shall be carried out by the Contractor at his own expense if the necessity thereof shall in the opinion of the Engineer be due to the use of materials or workmanship not in accordance with the Contract or to neglect or failure on the part of the Contractor to comply with any obligation expressed or implied on the Contractor's part under the Contract. If in the opinion of the Engineer such necessity shall be due to any other cause the value of such work shall be ascertained and paid for as if it were additional work.

**Remedy on Contractor's Failure to Carry out Work Required.**

(4) If the Contractor shall fail to do any such work as aforesaid required by the Engineer the Employer shall be entitled to carry out such work by his own workmen or by other contractors and if such work is work which the Contractor should have carried out at the Contractor's own cost shall be entitled to recover from the Contractor the cost thereof or may deduct the same from any monies due or that become due to the Contractor.

**Temporary Reinstatement.**

(5) Provided always that if in the course or for the purposes of the execution of the Works or any part thereof any highway or other road or way shall have been broken into then notwithstanding anything herein contained:—

(a) If the permanent reinstatement of such highway or other road or way is to be carried out by the appropriate Highway Authority or by some person other than the Contractor (or any sub-contractor to him) the Contractor shall at his own cost and independently of any requirement of or notice from the Engineer be responsible for the making good of any subsidence or shrinkage or other defect imperfection or fault in the temporary reinstatement of such highway or other road or way and for the execution of any necessary repair or amendment thereof from whatever cause the necessity arises until the end of the Period of Maintenance in respect of the works beneath such highway or other road or way or until the Highway Authority or other person as aforesaid shall have taken possession of the Site for the purpose of carrying out permanent reinstatement (whichever is the earlier) and shall indemnify and save harmless the Employer against and from any damage or injury to the Employer or to third parties arising out or in consequence of any neglect or failure of the Contractor to comply with the foregoing obligations or any of them and against and from all claims demands proceedings damages costs charges and expenses whatsoever in respect thereof or in relation thereto. As from the end of such Period of Maintenance or the taking of possession as aforesaid (whichever shall first happen) the Employer shall indemnify and save harmless the Contractor against and from any damage or injury as aforesaid arising out or in consequence of or in connection with the said permanent reinstatement or any defect imperfection or failure of or in such work of permanent reinstatement and against and from all claims demands proceedings damages costs charges and expenses whatsoever in respect thereof or in relation thereto.

(b) Where the Highway Authority or other person as aforesaid shall take possession of the Site as aforesaid in sections or lengths the responsibility of the Contractor under paragraph (a) of this sub-clause shall cease in regard to any such section or length at the time possession thereof is so taken but shall during the continuance of the said Period of Maintenance continue in regard to any length of which possession has not been so taken and the indemnities given by the Contractor and the Employer respectively under the said paragraph shall be construed and have effect accordingly.

**Contractor to Search.**

**50.** The Contractor shall if required by the Engineer in writing carry out such searches tests or trials as may be necessary to determine the cause of any defect imperfection or fault under the directions of the Engineer. Unless such defect imperfection or fault shall be one for which the Contractor is liable under the Contract the cost of the work carried out by the Contractor as aforesaid shall be borne by the Employer. But if such defect imperfection or fault shall be one for which the Contractor is liable the cost of the work carried out as aforesaid shall be borne by the Contractor and he shall in such case repair rectify and make good such defect imperfection or fault at his own expense in accordance with Clause 49.

# OUTSTANDING WORK AND DEFECTS

**Work outstanding** **49** (1) The undertaking to be given under Clause 48 (1) may after agreement between the Engineer and the Contractor specify a time or times within which the outstanding work shall be completed. If no such times are specified any outstanding work shall be completed as soon as practicable during the Defects Correction Period.

*New Clause concerning the completion of outstanding work at agreed times and also covers previous Clause 49(2) lines 4 and 5.*

**Execution of work of repair etc.** (2) The Contractor shall deliver up to the Employer the Works and each Section and part thereof at or as soon as practicable after the expiry of the relevant Defects Correction Period in the condition required by the Contract (fair wear and tear excepted) to the satisfaction of the Engineer. To this end the Contractor shall as soon as practicable execute all work of repair amendment reconstruction rectification and making good of defects of whatever nature as may be required of him in writing by the Engineer during the relevant Defects Correction Period or within 14 days after its expiry as a result of an inspection made by or on behalf of the Engineer prior to its expiry.

**Cost of execution of work of repair etc.** (3) All work required under sub-clause (2) of this Clause shall be carried out by the Contractor at his own expense if in the Engineer's opinion it is necessary due to the use of materials or workmanship not in accordance with the Contract or to neglect or failure by the Contractor to comply with any of his obligations under the Contract. In any other event the value of such work shall be ascertained and paid for as if it were additional work.

**Remedy on Contractor's failure to carry out work required** (4) If the Contractor fails to do any such work as aforesaid the Employer shall be entitled to carry out such work by his own workpeople or by other contractors and if such work is work which the Contractor should have carried out at his own expense the Employer shall be entitled to recover the cost thereof from the Contractor and may deduct the same from any monies that are or may become due to the Contractor.

*Previous Clause 49(5) concerning Temporary Reinstatement has been omitted.*

**Contractor to search** **50** The Contractor shall if required by the Engineer in writing carry out such searches tests or trials as may be necessary to determine the cause of any defect imperfection or fault under the directions of the Engineer. Unless such defect imperfection or fault shall be one for which the Contractor is liable under the Contract the cost of the work carried out by the Contractor as aforesaid shall be borne by the Employer. But if such defect imperfection or fault shall be one for which the Contractor is liable the cost of the work carried out as aforesaid shall be borne by the Contractor and he shall in such case repair rectify and make good such defect imperfection or fault at his own expense in accordance with Clause 49.

**5th**

**Ordered Variations.**

**51.** (1) The Engineer shall order any variation to any part of the Works that may in his opinion be necessary for the completion of the Works and shall have power to order any variation that for any other reason shall in his opinion be desirable for the satisfactory completion and functioning of the Works. Such variations may include additions omissions substitutions alterations changes in quality form character kind position dimension level or line and changes in the specified sequence method or timing of construction (if any).

**Ordered Variations to be in Writing.**

(2) No such variation shall be made by the Contractor without an order by the Engineer. All such orders shall be given in writing provided that if for any reason the Engineer shall find it necessary to give any such order orally in the first instance the Contractor shall comply with such oral order. Such oral order shall be confirmed in writing by the Engineer as soon as is possible in the circumstances. If the Contractor shall confirm in writing to the Engineer any oral order by the Engineer and such confirmation shall not be contradicted in writing by the Engineer forthwith it shall be deemed to be an order in writing by the Engineer. No variation ordered or deemed to be ordered in writing in accordance with sub-clauses (1) and (2) of this Clause shall in any way vitiate or invalidate the Contract but the value (if any) of all such variations shall be taken into account in ascertaining the amount of the Contract Price.

**Changes in Quantities.**

(3) No order in writing shall be required for increase or decrease in the quantity of any work where such increase or decrease is not the result of an order given under this Clause but is the result of the quantities exceeding or being less than those stated in the Bill of Quantities.

**Valuation of Ordered Variations.**

**52.** (1) The value of all variations ordered by the Engineer in accordance with Clause 51 shall be ascertained by the Engineer after consultation with the Contractor in accordance with the following principles. Where work is of similar character and executed under similar conditions to work priced in the Bill of Quantities it shall be valued at such rates and prices contained therein as may be applicable. Where work is not of a similar character or is not executed under similar conditions the rates and prices in the Bill of Quantities shall be used as the basis for valuation so far as may be reasonable failing which a fair valuation shall be made. Failing agreement between the Engineer and the Contractor as to any rate or price to be applied in the valuation of any variation the Engineer shall determine the rate or price in accordance with the foregoing principles and he shall notify the Contractor accordingly.

## ALTERATIONS, ADDITIONS AND OMISSIONS

**Ordered variations**

**51** (1) The Engineer

(a) shall order any variation to any part of the Works that is in his opinion necessary for the completion of the Works and

(b) may order any variation that for any other reason shall in his opinion be desirable for the completion and/or improved functioning of the Works.

Such variations may include additions omissions substitutions alterations changes in quality form character kind position dimension level or line and changes in any specified sequence method or timing of construction required by the Contract and may be ordered during the Defects Correction Period.

*This Clause has been extended to include variations ordered after substantial completion.*

**Ordered variations to be in writing**

(2) All variations shall be ordered in writing but the provisions of Clause 2(6) in respect of oral instructions shall apply.

**Variation not to affect Contract**

(3) No variation ordered in accordance with sub-clauses (1) and (2) of this Clause shall in any way vitiate or invalidate the Contract but the value (if any) of all such variations shall be taken into account in ascertaining the amount of the Contract Price except to the extent that such variation is necessitated by the Contractor's default.

*A qualification has been added in respect of variations necessitated by the Contractor's default.*

**Changes in quantities**

(4) No order in writing shall be required for increase or decrease in the quantity of any work where such increase or decrease is not the result of an order given under this Clause but is the result of the quantities exceeding or being less than those stated in the Bill of Quantities.

**Valuation of ordered variations**

**52** (1) The value of all variations ordered by the Engineer in accordance with Clause 51 shall be ascertained by the Engineer after consultation with the Contractor in accordance with the following principles.

(a) Where work is of similar character and executed under similar conditions to work priced in the Bill of Quantities it shall be valued at such rates and prices contained therein as may be applicable.

(b) Where work is not of a similar character or is not executed under similar conditions or is ordered during the Defects Correction Period the rates and prices in the Bill of Quantities shall be used as the basis for valuation so far as may be reasonable failing which a fair valuation shall be made.

Failing agreement between the Engineer and the Contractor as to any rate or price to be applied in the valuation of any variation the Engineer shall determine the rate or price in accordance with the foregoing principles and he shall notify the Contractor accordingly.

*This sub-clause makes it clear that Bill of Quantity rates do not necessarily apply to work ordered after substantial completion.*

**Engineer to fix Rates.**

(2)   Provided that if the nature or amount of any variation relative to the nature or amount of the whole of the contract work or to any part thereof shall be such that in the opinion of the Engineer or the Contractor any rate or price contained in the Contract for any item of work is by reason of such variation rendered unreasonable or inapplicable either the Engineer shall give to the Contractor or the Contractor shall give to the Engineer notice before the varied work is commenced or as soon thereafter as is reasonable in all the circumstances that such rate or price should be varied and the Engineer shall fix such rate or price as in the circumstances he shall think reasonable and proper.

**Daywork.**

(3)   The Engineer may if in his opinion it is necessary or desirable order in writing that any additional or substituted work shall be executed on a daywork basis.   The Contractor shall then be paid for such work under the conditions set out in the Daywork Schedule included in the Bill of Quantities and at the rates and prices affixed thereto by him in his Tender and failing the provision of a Daywork Schedule he shall be paid at the rates and prices and under the conditions contained in the " Schedules of Dayworks carried out incidental to Contract Work " issued by The Federation of Civil Engineering Contractors current at the date of the execution of the Daywork.

The Contractor shall furnish to the Engineer such receipts or other vouchers as may be necessary to prove the amounts paid and before ordering materials shall submit to the Engineer quotations for the same for his approval.

In respect of all work executed on a daywork basis the Contractor shall during the continuance of such work deliver each day to the Engineer's Representative an exact list in duplicate of the names occupation and time of all workmen employed on such work and a statement also in duplicate showing the description and quantity of all materials and plant used thereon or therefor (other than plant which is included in the percentage addition in accordance with the Schedule under which payment for daywork is made).   One copy of each list and statement will if correct or when agreed be signed by the Engineer's Representative and returned to the Contractor.   At the end of each month the Contractor shall deliver to the Engineer's Representative a priced statement of the labour material and plant (except as aforesaid) used and the Contractor shall not be entitled to any payment unless such lists and statements have been fully and punctually rendered. Provided always that if the Engineer shall consider that for any reason the sending of such list or statement by the Contractor in accordance with the foregoing provision was impracticable he shall nevertheless be entitled to authorise payment for such work either as daywork (on being satisfied as to the time employed and plant and materials used on such work) or at such value therefor as he shall consider fair and reasonable.

**Notice of Claims.**

(4) (a) If the Contractor intends to claim a higher rate or price than one notified to him by the Engineer pursuant to sub-clauses (1) and (2) of this Clause or Clause 56(2) the Contractor shall within 28 days after such notification give notice in writing of his intention to the Engineer.

(b) If the Contractor intends to claim any additional payment pursuant to any Clause of these Conditions other than sub-clauses (1) and (2) of this Clause he shall give notice in writing of his intention to the Engineer as soon as reasonably possible after the happening of the events giving rise to the claim.   Upon the happening of such events the Contractor shall keep such contemporary records as may reasonably be necessary to support any claim he may subsequently wish to make.

(c) Without necessarily admitting the Employer's liability the Engineer may upon receipt of a notice under this Clause instruct the Contractor to keep such contemporary records or further contemporary records as the case may be as are reasonable and may be material to the claim of which notice has been given and the Contractor shall keep such records.   The Contractor shall permit the Engineer to inspect all records kept pursuant to this Clause and shall supply him with copies thereof as and when the Engineer shall so instruct.

(d) After the giving of a notice to the Engineer under this Clause the Contractor shall as soon as is reasonable in all the circumstances send to the Engineer a first interim account giving full and detailed particulars of the amount claimed to that date and of the grounds upon which the claim is based.   Thereafter at such intervals as the Engineer may reasonably require the Contractor shall send to the Engineer further up to date accounts giving the accumulated total of the claim and any further grounds upon which it is based.

(e) If the Contractor fails to comply with any of the provisions of this Clause in respect of any claim which he shall seek to make then the Contractor shall be entitled to payment in respect thereof only to the extent that the Engineer has not been prevented from or substantially prejudiced by such failure in investigating the said claim.

**Engineer to fix rates**

(2) If the nature or amount of any variation relative to the nature or amount of the whole of the contract work or to any part thereof shall be such that in the opinion of the Engineer or the Contractor any rate or price contained in the Contract for any item of work is by reason of such variation rendered unreasonable or inapplicable either the Engineer shall give to the Contractor or the Contractor shall give to the Engineer notice before the varied work is commenced or as soon thereafter as is reasonable in all the circumstances that such rate or price should be varied and the Engineer shall fix such rate or price as in the circumstances he shall think reasonable and proper.

**Daywork**

(3) The Engineer may if in his opinion it is necessary or desirable order in writing that any additional or substituted work shall be executed on a daywork basis in accordance with the provisions of Clause 56(4).

*As previous first two lines of Clause 52(3) but then referring to Clause 56(4) for the actual daywork procedure.*

**Notice of claims**

(4) (a) If the Contractor intends to claim a higher rate or price than one notified to him by the Engineer pursuant to sub-clauses (1) and (2) of this Clause or Clause 56(2) the Contractor shall within 28 days after such notification give notice in writing of his intention to the Engineer.

(b) If the Contractor intends to claim any additional payment pursuant to any Clause of these Conditions other than sub-clauses (1) and (2) of this Clause or Clause 56(2) he shall give notice in writing of his intention to the Engineer as soon as may be reasonable and in any event within 28 days after the happening of the events giving rise to the claim. Upon the happening of such events the Contractor shall keep such contemporary records as may reasonably be necessary to support any claim he may subsequently wish to make.

(c) Without necessarily admitting the Employer's liability the Engineer may upon receipt of a notice under this Clause instruct the Contractor to keep such contemporary records or further contemporary records as the case may be as are reasonable and may be material to the claim of which notice has been given and the Contractor shall keep such records. The Contractor shall permit the Engineer to inspect all records kept pursuant to this Clause and shall supply him with copies thereof as and when the Engineer shall so instruct.

(d) After the giving of a notice to the Engineer under this Clause the Contractor shall as soon as is reasonable in all the circumstances send to the Engineer a first interim account giving full and detailed particulars of the amount claimed to that date and of the grounds upon which the claim is based. Thereafter at such intervals as the Engineer may reasonably require the Contractor shall send to the Engineer further up to date accounts giving the accumulated total of the claim and any further grounds upon which it is based.

(e) If the Contractor fails to comply with any of the provisions of this Clause in respect of any claim which he shall seek to make then the Contractor shall be entitled to payment in respect thereof only to the extent that the Engineer has not been prevented from or substantially prejudiced by such failure in investigating the said claim.

(f) The Contractor shall be entitled to have included in any interim payment certified by the Engineer pursuant to Clause 60 such amount in respect of any claim as the Engineer may consider due to the Contractor provided that the Contractor shall have supplied sufficient particulars to enable the Engineer to determine the amount due. If such particulars are insufficient to substantiate the whole of the claim the Contractor shall be entitled to payment in respect of such part of the claim as the particulars may substantiate to the satisfaction of the Engineer.

## PROPERTY IN MATERIALS AND PLANT

**Plant, etc.—Definitions.**

53. (1) For the purpose of this Clause:—

    (a) the expression " Plant " shall mean any Constructional Plant Temporary Works and materials for Temporary Works but shall exclude any vehicles engaged in transporting any labour plant or materials to or from the Site;

    (b) the expression " agreement for hire " shall be deemed not to include an agreement for hire purchase.

**Vesting of Plant.**

(2) All Plant goods and materials owned by the Contractor or by any company in which the Contractor has a controlling interest shall when on the Site be deemed to be the property of the Employer.

**Conditions of Hire of Plant.**

(3) With a view to securing in the event of a forfeiture under Clause 63 the continued availability for the purpose of executing the Works of any hired Plant the Contractor shall not bring on to the Site any hired Plant unless there is an agreement for the hire thereof which contains a provision that the owner thereof will on request in writing made by the Employer within 7 days after the date on which any forfeiture has become effective and on the Employer undertaking to pay all hire charges in respect thereof from such date hire such Plant to the Employer on the same terms in all respects as the same was hired to the Contractor save that the Employer shall be entitled to permit the use thereof by any other contractor employed by him for the purpose of completing the Works under the terms of the said Clause 63.

**Costs for Purposes of Clause 63.**

(4) In the event of the Employer entering into any agreement for the hire of Plant pursuant to sub-clause (3) of this Clause all sums properly paid by the Employer under the provisions of any such agreement and all expenses incurred by him (including stamp duties) in entering into such agreement shall be deemed for the purpose of Clause 63 to be part of the cost of completing the Works.

**Notification of Plant Ownership.**

(5) The Contractor shall upon request made by the Engineer at any time in relation to any item of Plant forthwith notify to the Engineer in writing the name and address of the owner thereof and shall in the case of hired Plant certify that the agreement for the hire thereof contains a provision in accordance with the requirements of sub-clause (3) of this Clause.

**Irremovability of Plant, etc.**

(6) No Plant (except hired Plant) goods or materials or any part thereof shall be removed from the Site without the written consent of the Engineer which consent shall not be unreasonably withheld where the same are no longer immediately required for the purposes of the completion of the Works but the Employer will permit the Contractor the exclusive use of all such Plant goods and materials in and for the completion of the Works until the occurrence of any event which gives the Employer the right to exclude the Contractor from the Site and proceed with the completion of the Works.

**Revesting and Removal of Plant.**

(7) Upon the removal of any such Plant goods or materials as have been deemed to have become the property of the Employer under sub-clause (2) of this Clause with the consent as aforesaid the property therein shall be deemed to revest in the Contractor and upon completion of the Works the property in the remainder of such Plant goods and materials as aforesaid shall subject to Clause 63 be deemed to revest in the Contractor.

**Disposal of Plant.**

(8) If the Contractor shall fail to remove any Plant goods or materials as required pursuant to Clause 33 within such reasonable time after completion of the Works as may be allowed by the Engineer then the Employer may:—

    (a) sell any which are the property of the Contractor; and

    (b) return any not the property of the Contractor to the owner thereof at the Contractor's expense;

and after deducting from any proceeds of sale the costs charges and expenses of and in connection with such sale and of and in connection with return as aforesaid shall pay the balance (if any) to the Contractor but to the extent that the proceeds of any sale are insufficient to meet all such costs charges and expenses the excess shall be a debt due from the Contractor to the Employer and shall be deductible or recoverable by the Employer from any monies due or that may become due to the Contractor under the contract or may be recovered by the Employer from the Contractor at law.

(f) The Contractor shall be entitled to have included in any interim payment certified by the Engineer pursuant to Clause 60 such amount in respect of any claim as the Engineer may consider due to the Contractor provided that the Contractor shall have supplied sufficient particulars to enable the Engineer to determine the amount due. If such particulars are insufficient to substantiate the whole of the claim the Contractor shall be entitled to payment in respect of such part of the claim as the particulars may substantiate to the satisfaction of the Engineer.

## PROPERTY IN MATERIALS AND CONTRACTOR'S EQUIPMENT

**Vesting of Contractor's Equipment**

**53** (1) All Contractor's Equipment Temporary Works materials for Temporary Works or other goods or materials owned by the Contractor shall when on Site be deemed to be the property of the Employer and shall not be removed therefrom without the written consent of the Engineer which consent shall not unreasonably be withheld where the items in question are no longer immediately required for the purposes of the completion of the Works.

*Generally as previous Clauses 53(2) and the first four lines of Clause 53(6) but restricted to Equipment owned by the Contractor.*

**Liability for loss or damage to Contractor's Equipment**

(2) The Employer shall not at any time be liable save as mentioned in Clauses 22 and 65 for the loss of or damage to any Contractor's Equipment Temporary Works goods or materials.

*Substantially as previous Clauses 53(9).*

**Disposal of Contractor's Equipment**

(3) If the Contractor fails to remove any of the said Contractor's Equipment Temporary Works goods or materials as required by Clause 33 within such reasonable time after completion of the Works as the Engineer may allow then the Employer may sell or otherwise dispose of such items. From the proceeds of the sale of any such items the Employer shall be entitled to retain any costs or expenses incurred in connection with their sale and disposal before paying the balance (if any) to the Contractor.

*Substantially as previous Clause 53(8).*

**Liability for Loss or Injury to Plant.**

(9) The Employer shall not at any time be liable for the loss of or injury to any of the Plant goods or materials which have been deemed to become the property of the Employer under sub-clause (2) of this Clause save as mentioned in Clauses 20 and 65.

**Incorporation of Clause in Sub-contracts.**

(10) The Contractor shall where entering into any sub-contract for the execution of any part of the Works incorporate in such sub-contract (by reference or otherwise) the provisions of this Clause in relation to Plant goods or materials brought on to the Site by the sub-contractor.

**No Approval by Vesting.**

(11) The operation of this Clause shall not be deemed to imply any approval by the Engineer of the materials or other matters referred to herein nor shall it prevent the rejection of any such materials at any time by the Engineer.

**Vesting of Goods and Materials not on Site.**

54. (1) The Contractor may with a view to securing payment under Clause 60(1)(c) in respect of goods and materials listed in the Appendix to the Form of Tender before the same are delivered to the Site transfer the property in the same to the Employer before delivery to the Site provided:—

    (a) that such goods and materials have been manufactured or prepared and are substantially ready for incorporation in the Works; and

    (b) that the said goods and materials are the property of the Contractor or the contract for the supply of the same expressly provides that the property therein shall pass unconditionally to the Contractor upon the Contractor taking the action referred to in sub-clause (2) of this Clause.

**Action by Contractor.**

(2) The intention of the Contractor to transfer the property in any goods or materials to the Employer in accordance with this Clause shall be evidenced by the Contractor taking or causing the supplier of the said goods or materials to take the following action:—

    (a) provide to the Engineer documentary evidence that the property in the said goods or materials has vested in the Contractor;

    (b) suitably mark or otherwise plainly identify the said goods and materials so as to show that their destination is the Site that they are the property of the Employer and (where they are not stored at the premises of the Contractor) to whose order they are held;

    (c) set aside and store the said goods and materials so marked or identified to the satisfaction of the Engineer; and

    (d) send to the Engineer a schedule listing and giving the value of every item of the goods and materials so set aside and stored and inviting him to inspect the same.

**Vesting in Employer.**

(3) Upon the Engineer approving in writing the said goods and materials for the purposes of this Clause the same shall vest in and become the absolute property of the Employer and thereafter shall be in the possession of the Contractor for the sole purpose of delivering them to the Employer and incorporating them in the Works and shall not be within the ownership control or disposition of the Contractor.

Provided always that:—

    (a) approval by the Engineer for the purposes of this Clause or any payment certified by him in respect of goods and materials pursuant to Clause 60 shall be without prejudice to the exercise of any power of the Engineer contained in this Contract to reject any goods or materials which are not in accordance with the provisions of the Contract and upon any such rejection the property in the rejected goods or materials shall immediately revest in the Contractor;

    (b) the Contractor shall be responsible for any loss or damage to such goods and materials and for the cost of storing handling and transporting the same and shall effect such additional insurance as may be necessary to cover the risk of such loss or damage from any cause.

**Vesting of goods and materials not on Site**

**54** (1) With a view to securing payment under Clause 60(1)(c) the Contractor may (and shall if the Engineer so directs) transfer to the Employer the property in goods and materials listed in the Appendix to the Form of Tender before the same are delivered to the Site provided that the goods and materials

(a) have been manufactured or prepared and are substantially ready for incorporation in the Works and

(b) are the property of the Contractor or the contract for the supply of the same expressly provides that the property therein shall pass unconditionally to the Contractor upon the Contractor taking the action referred to in sub-clause (2) of this Clause.

*Clauses substantially as previous Clause 54 but including provision in Clause 54(1) for the Engineer to direct that there shall be vesting.*

**Action by Contractor**

(2) The intention of the Contractor to transfer the property in any goods or materials to the Employer in accordance with this Clause shall be evidenced by the Contractor taking or causing the supplier of those goods or materials to take the following actions.

(a) Provide to the Engineer documentary evidence that the property in the said goods or materials has vested in the Contractor.

(b) Suitably mark or otherwise plainly identify the goods and materials so as to show that their destination is the Site that they are the property of the Employer and (where they are not stored at the premises of the Contractor) to whose order they are held.

(c) Set aside and store the said goods and materials so marked or identified to the satisfaction of the Engineer.

(d) Send to the Engineer a schedule listing and giving the value of every item of the goods and materials so set aside and stored and inviting him to inspect them.

**Vesting in Employer**

(3) Upon the Engineer approving in writing the transfer in ownership of any goods and materials for the purposes of this Clause they shall vest in and become the absolute property of the Employer and thereafter shall be in possession of the Contractor for the sole purpose of delivering them to the Employer and incorporating them in the Works and shall not be within the ownership control or disposition of the Contractor.

Provided always that

(a) approval by the Engineer for the purposes of this Clause or any payment certified by him in respect of goods and materials pursuant to Clause 60 shall be without prejudice to the exercise of any power of the Engineer contained in this Contract to reject any goods or materials which are not in accordance with the provisions of the Contract and upon any such rejection the property in the rejected goods or materials shall immediately revest in the Contractor and

(b) the Contractor shall be responsible for any loss or damage to such goods and materials and for the cost of storing handling and transporting the same and shall effect such additional insurance as may be necessary to cover the risk of such loss or damage from any cause.

**Lien on Goods or Materials.**

(4)   Neither the Contractor nor a sub-contractor nor any other person shall have a lien on any goods or materials which have vested in the Employer under sub-clause (3) of this Clause for any sum due to the Contractor sub-contractor or other person and the Contractor shall take all such steps as may reasonably be necessary to ensure that the title of the Employer and the exclusion of any such lien are brought to the notice of sub-contractors and other persons dealing with any such goods or materials.

**Delivery to the Employer of Vested Goods or Materials.**

(5)   Upon cessation of the employment of the Contractor under this contract before the completion of the Works whether as a result of the operation of Clause 63 or otherwise the Contractor shall deliver to the Employer any goods or materials the property in which has vested in the Employer by virtue of sub-clause (3) of this Clause and if he shall fail to do so the Employer may enter any premises of the Contractor or of any sub-contractor and remove such goods and materials and recover the cost of so doing from the Contractor.

**Incorporation in Sub-contracts.**

(6)   The Contractor shall incorporate provisions equivalent to those provided in this Clause in every sub-contract in which provision is to be made for payment in respect of goods or materials before the same have been delivered to the Site.

## MEASUREMENT

**Quantities.**

55.   (1)   The quantities set out in the Bill of Quantities are the estimated quantities of the work but they are not to be taken as the actual and correct quantities of the Works to be executed by the Contractor in fulfilment of his obligations under the Contract.

**Correction of Errors.**

(2)   Any error in description in the Bill of Quantities or omission therefrom shall not vitiate the Contract nor release the Contractor from the execution of the whole or any part of the Works according to the Drawings and Specification or from any of his obligations or liabilities under the Contract.   Any such error or omission shall be corrected by the Engineer and the value of the work actually carried out shall be ascertained in accordance with Clause 52.   Provided that there shall be no rectification of any errors omissions or wrong estimates in the descriptions rates and prices inserted by the Contractor in the Bill of Quantities.

**Measurement and Valuation.**

56.   (1)   The Engineer shall except as otherwise stated ascertain and determine by admeasurement the value in accordance with the Contract of the work done in accordance with the Contract.

**Increase or Decrease of Rate.**

(2)   Should the actual quantities executed in respect of any item be greater or less than those stated in the Bill of Quantities and if in the opinion of the Engineer such increase or decrease of itself shall so warrant the Engineer shall after consultation with the Contractor determine an appropriate increase or decrease of any rates or prices rendered unreasonable or inapplicable in consequence thereof and shall notify the Contractor accordingly.

**Attending for Measurement.**

(3)   The Engineer shall when he requires any part or parts of the work to be measured give reasonable notice to the Contractor who shall attend or send a qualified agent to assist the Engineer or the Engineer's Representative in making such measurement and shall furnish all particulars required by either of them.   Should the Contractor not attend or neglect or omit to send such agent then the measurement made by the Engineer or approved by him shall be taken to be the correct measurement of the work.

**Lien on goods or materials**

(4)    Neither the Contractor nor a sub-contractor nor any other person shall have a lien on any goods or materials which have vested in the Employer under sub-clause (3) of this Clause for any sum due to the Contractor sub-contractor or other person and the Contractor shall take all such steps as may reasonably be necessary to ensure that the title of the Employer and the exclusion of any such lien are brought to the notice of sub-contractors and other persons dealing with any such goods or materials.

**Delivery to the Employer of vested goods or materials**

(5)    Upon cessation of the employment of the Contractor under this Contract before the completion of the Works whether as a result of the operation of Clause 63 or otherwise the Contractor shall deliver to the Employer any goods or materials the property in which has vested in the Employer by virtue of sub-clause (3) of this Clause and if he shall fail to do so the Employer may enter any premises of the Contractor or of any sub-contractor and remove such goods and materials and recover the cost of so doing from the Contractor.

**Incorporation in sub-contracts**

(6)    The Contractor shall incorporate provisions equivalent to those provided in this Clause in every sub-contract in which provision is to be made for payment in respect of goods or materials before the same have been delivered to the Site.

## MEASUREMENT

**Quantities  55**

(1)    The quantities set out in the Bill of Quantities are the estimated quantities of the work but they are not to be taken as the actual and correct quantities of the Works to be executed by the Contractor in fulfilment of his obligations under the Contract.

**Correction of errors**

(2)    Any error in description in the Bill of Quantities or omission therefrom shall not vitiate the Contract nor release the Contractor from the execution of the whole or any part of the Works according to the Drawings and Specification or from any of his obligations or liabilities under the Contract. Any such error or omission shall be corrected by the Engineer and the value of the work actually carried out shall be ascertained in accordance with Clause 52. Provided that there shall be no rectification of any errors omissions or wrong estimates in the descriptions rates and prices inserted by the Contractor in the Bill of Quantities.

**Measurement and  56 valuation**

(1)    The Engineer shall except as otherwise stated ascertain and determine by admeasurement the value in accordance with the Contract of the work done in accordance with the Contract.

**Increase or decrease of rate**

(2)    Should the actual quantities executed in respect of any item be greater or less than those stated in the Bill of Quantities and if in the opinion of the Engineer such increase or decrease of itself shall so warrant the Engineer shall after consultation with the Contractor determine an appropriate increase or decrease of any rates or prices rendered unreasonable or inapplicable in consequence thereof and shall notify the Contractor accordingly.

**Attending for measurement**

(3)    The Engineer shall when he requires any part or parts of the work to be measured give reasonable notice to the Contractor who shall attend or send a qualified agent to assist the Engineer or the Engineer's Representative in making such measurement and shall furnish all particulars required by either of them. Should the Contractor not attend or neglect or omit to send such agent then the measurement made by the Engineer or approved by him shall be taken to be the correct measurement of the work.

**Method of Measurement.**

57. Except where any statement or general or detailed description of the work in the Bill of Quantities expressly shows to the contrary Bills of Quantities shall be deemed to have been prepared and measurements shall be made according to the procedure set forth in the " Civil Engineering Standard Method of Measurement " approved by the Institution of Civil Engineers and the Federation of Civil Engineering Contractors in association with the Association of Consulting Engineers in 1976 or such later or amended edition thereof as may be stated in the Appendix to the Form of Tender to have been adopted in its preparation notwithstanding any general or local custom.

## PROVISIONAL AND PRIME COST SUMS AND NOMINATED SUB-CONTRACTS

**Provisional Sum.**

58. (1) " Provisional Sum " means a sum included in the Contract and so designated for the execution of work or the supply of goods materials or services or for contingencies which sum may be used in whole or in part or not at all at the direction and discretion of the Engineer.

**Prime Cost Item.**

(2) " Prime Cost (PC) Item " means an item in the Contract which contains (either wholly or in part) a sum referred to as Prime Cost (PC) which will be used for the execution of work or for the supply of goods materials or services for the Works.

**Design Requirements to be Expressly Stated.**

(3) If in connection with any Provisional Sum or Prime Cost Item the services to be provided include any matter of design or specification of any part of the Permanent Works or of any equipment or plant to be incorporated therein such requirement shall be expressly stated in the Contract and shall be included in any Nominated Sub-contract. The obligation of the Contractor in respect thereof shall be only that which has been expressly stated in accordance with this sub-clause.

**Use of Prime Cost Items.**

(4) In respect of every Prime Cost Item the Engineer shall have power to order the Contractor to employ a sub-contractor nominated by the Engineer for the execution of any work or the supply of any goods materials or services included therein. The Engineer shall also have power with the consent of the Contractor to order the Contractor to execute any such work or to supply any such goods materials or services in which event the Contractor shall be paid in accordance with the terms of a quotation submitted by him and accepted by the Engineer or in the absence thereof the value shall be determined in accordance with Clause 52.

**Daywork**

(4)    Where any work is carried out on a daywork basis the Contractor shall be paid for such work under the conditions and at the rates and prices set out in the daywork schedule included in the Contract or failing the inclusion of a daywork schedule he shall be paid at the rates and prices and under the conditions contained in the "Schedule of Dayworks carried out incidental to Contract Work" issued by The Federation of Civil Engineering Contractors current at the date of the execution of the daywork.

The Contractor shall furnish to the Engineer such records receipts and other documentation as may be necessary to prove amounts paid and/or costs incurred. Such returns shall be in the form and delivered at the times the Engineer shall direct and shall be agreed within a reasonable time.

Before ordering materials the Contractor shall if so required submit to the Engineer quotations for the same for his approval.

*New Clause substantially taken from previous Clause 52(3) but reworded and simplified in respect of the returns required, these to be as required by the Engineer who may also require quotations for materials before they are ordered.*

**Method of measurement**

**57**    Unless otherwise provided in the Contract or unless general or detailed description of the work in the Bill of Quantities or any other statement clearly shows to the contrary the Bill of Quantities shall be deemed to have been prepared and measurements shall be made according to the procedure set out in the "Civil Engineering Standard Method of Measurement Second Edition 1985" approved by the Institution of Civil Engineers and the Federation of Civil Engineering Contractors in association with the Association of Consulting Engineers or such later or amended edition thereof as may be stated in the Appendix to the Form of Tender to have been adopted in its preparation.

*Substantially as previous Clause 57 but updated with respect to the "Civil Engineering Standard Method of Measurement" and exception noted where Bills of Quantities show to the contrary.*

## PROVISIONAL AND PRIME COST SUMS AND NOMINATED SUB-CONTRACTS

*The definitions of Provisional Sums, Prime Cost Items and Nominated Sub-Contractors have been moved to Clause 1(1).*

**Use of Provisional Sums**

**58**    (1)    In respect of every Provisional Sum the Engineer may order either or both of the following.

(a) Work to be executed or goods materials or services to be supplied by the Contractor the value thereof being determined in accordance with Clause 52 and included in the Contract Price.
(b) Work to be executed or goods materials or services to be supplied by a Nominated Sub-contractor in accordance with Clause 59.

*As previous Clause 58(7).*

**Use of Prime Cost Items**

(2)    In respect of every Prime Cost Item the Engineer may order either or both of the following.

(a) Subject to Clause 59 that the Contractor employ a sub-contractor nominated by the Engineer for the execution of any work or the supply of any goods materials or services included therein.

**Nominated Sub-contractors— Definition.**

(5)   All specialists merchants tradesmen and others nominated in the Contract for a Prime Cost Item or ordered by the Engineer to be employed by the Contractor in accordance with sub-clause (4) or sub-clause (7) of this Clause for the execution of any work or the supply of any goods materials or services are referred to in this Contract as " Nominated Sub-contractors ".

**Production of Vouchers, etc.**

(6)   The Contractor shall when required by the Engineer produce all quotations invoices vouchers sub-contract documents accounts and receipts in connection with expenditure in respect of work carried out by all Nominated Sub-contractors.

**Use of Provisional Sums.**

(7)   In respect of every Provisional Sum the Engineer shall have power to order either or both of the following:—

(a)   work to be executed or goods materials or services to be supplied by the Contractor the value of such work executed or goods materials or services supplied being determined in accordance with Clause 52 and included in the Contract Price;

(b)   work to be executed or goods materials or services to be supplied by a Nominated Sub-contractor in accordance with Clause 59A.

**Nominated Sub-contractors— Objection to Nomination.**

**59A.** (1)   Subject to sub-clause (2)(c) of this Clause the Contractor shall not be under any obligation to enter into any sub-contract with any Nominated Sub-contractor against whom the Contractor may raise reasonable objection or who shall decline to enter into a sub-contract with the Contractor containing provisions:—

(a)   that in respect of the work goods materials or services the subject of the sub-contract the Nominated Sub-contractor will undertake towards the Contractor such obligations and liabilities as will enable the Contractor to discharge his own obligations and liabilities towards the Employer under the terms of the Contract;

(b)   that the Nominated Sub-contractor will save harmless and indemnify the Contractor against all claims demands and proceedings damages costs charges and expenses whatsoever arising out of or in connection with any failure by the Nominated Sub-contractor to perform such obligations or fulfil such liabilities;

(c)   that the Nominated Sub-contractor will save harmless and indemnify the Contractor from and against any negligence by the Nominated Sub-contractor his agents workmen and servants and against any misuse by him or them of any Constructional Plant or Temporary Works provided by the Contractor for the purposes of the Contract and for all claims as aforesaid;

(d)   equivalent to those contained in Clause 63.

**Engineer's Action upon Objection.**

(2)   If pursuant to sub-clause (1) of this Clause the Contractor shall not be obliged to enter into a sub-contract with a Nominated Sub-contractor and shall decline to do so the Engineer shall do one or more of the following:—

(a)   nominate an alternative sub-contractor in which case sub-clause (1) of this Clause shall apply;

(b)   by order under Clause 51 vary the Works or the work goods materials or services the subject of the Provisional Sum or Prime Cost Item including if necessary the omission of any such work goods materials or services so that they may be provided by workmen contractors or suppliers as the case may be employed by the Employer either concurrently with the Works (in which case Clause 31 shall apply) or at some other date.   Provided that in respect of the omission of any Prime Cost Item there shall be included in the Contract Price a sum in respect of the Contractor's charges and profit being a percentage of the estimated value of such work goods material or services omitted at the rate provided in the Bill of Quantities or inserted in the Appendix to the Form of Tender as the case may be;

(c)   subject to the Employer's consent where the Contractor declines to enter into a contract with the Nominated Sub-contractor only on the grounds of unwillingness of the Nominated Sub-contractor to contract on the basis of the provisions contained in paragraphs (a) (b) (c) or (d) of sub-clause (1) of this Clause direct the Contractor to enter into a contract with the Nominated Sub-contractor on such other terms as the Engineer shall specify in which case sub-clause (3) of this Clause shall apply;

(d)   in accordance with Clause 58 arrange for the Contractor to execute such work or to supply such goods materials or services.

(b) With the consent of the Contractor that the Contractor himself execute any such work or supply any such goods materials or services in which event the Contractor shall be paid in accordance with the terms of a quotation submitted by him and accepted by the Engineer or in the absence thereof the value shall be determined in accordance with Clause 52 and included in the Contract Price.

*Substantially as previous Clause 58(4).*

**Design requirements to be expressly stated**

(3) If in connection with any Provisional Sum or Prime Cost Item the services to be provided include any matter of design or specification of any part of the Permanent Works or of any equipment or plant to be incorporated therein such requirement shall be expressly stated in the Contract and shall be included in any Nominated Sub-contract. The obligation of the Contractor in respect thereof shall be only that which has been expressly stated in accordance with this sub-clause.

*As previous Clause 58(3).*

**Nominated Sub-contractors—objection to nomination**

**59** (1) The Contractor shall not be under any obligation to enter into a sub-contract with any Nominated Sub-contractor against whom the Contractor may raise reasonable objection or who declines to enter into a sub-contract with the Contractor containing provisions

(a) that in respect of the work goods materials or services the subject of the sub-contract the Nominated Sub-contractor will undertake towards the Contractor such obligations and liabilities as will enable the Contractor to discharge his own obligations and liabilities towards the Employer under the terms of the Contract

(b) that the Nominated Sub-contractor will save harmless and indemnify the Contractor against all claims demands and proceedings damages costs charges and expenses whatsoever arising out of or in connection with any failure by the Nominated Sub-contractor to perform such obligations or fulfil such liabilities

(c) that the Nominated Sub-contractor will save harmless and indemnify the Contractor from and against any negligence by the Nominated Sub-contractor his agents workmen and servants and against any misuse by him or them of any Contractor's Equipment or Temporary Works provided by the Contractor for the purposes of the Contract and for all claims as aforesaid

(d) that the Nominated Sub-contractor will provide the Contractor with security for the proper performance of the sub-contract and

(e) equivalent to those contained in Clause 63.

*As previous Clause 59A(1) but without the opening proviso that it is subject to sub-clause (2)(c). Sub-clause (2)(d) has been added under which the Contractor can require the Nominated Sub-Contractor to provide security for the performance of the Sub-contract.*

**Engineer's action upon objection to nomination or upon determination of Nominated Sub-contract**

(2) If pursuant to sub-clause (1) of this Clause the Contractor declines to enter into a sub-contract with a sub-contractor nominated by the Engineer or if during the course of the Nominated Sub-contract the Contractor shall validly terminate the employment of the Nominated Sub-contractor as a result of his default the Engineer shall

(a) nominate an alternative sub-contractor in which case sub-clause (1) of this Clause shall apply or

**Direction by Engineer.**

(3) If the Engineer shall direct the Contractor pursuant to sub-clause (2) of this Clause to enter into a sub-contract which does not contain all the provisions referred to in sub-clause (1) of this Clause:—

    (a) the Contractor shall not be bound to discharge his obligations and liabilities under the Contract to the extent that the sub-contract terms so specified by the Engineer are inconsistent with the discharge of the same;

    (b) in the event of the Contractor incurring loss or expense or suffering damage arising out of the refusal of the Nominated Sub-contractor to accept such provisions the Contractor shall subject to Clause 52(4) be paid in accordance with Clause 60 the amount of such loss expense or damage as the Contractor could not reasonably avoid.

**Contractor Responsible for Nominated Sub-contracts.**

(4) Except as otherwise provided in this Clause and in Clause 59B the Contractor shall be as responsible for the work executed or goods materials or services supplied by a Nominated Sub-contractor employed by him as if he had himself executed such work or supplied such goods materials or services or had sub-let the same in accordance with Clause 4.

**Payments.**

(5) For all work executed or goods materials or services supplied by Nominated Sub-contractors there shall be included in the Contract Price:—

    (a) the actual price paid or due to be paid by the Contractor in accordance with the terms of the sub-contract (unless and to the extent that any such payment is the result of a default of the Contractor) net of all trade and other discounts rebates and allowances other than any discount obtainable by the Contractor for prompt payment;

    (b) the sum (if any) provided in the Bill of Quantities for labours in connection therewith or if ordered pursuant to Clause 58(7)(b) as may be determined by the Engineer;

    (c) in respect of all other charges and profit a sum being a percentage of the actual price paid or due to be paid calculated (where provision has been made in the Bill of Quantities for a rate to be set against the relevant item of prime cost) at the rate inserted by the Contractor against that item or (where no such provision has been made) at the rate inserted by the Contractor in the Appendix to the Form of Tender as the percentage for adjustment of sums set against Prime Cost Items.

**Breach of Sub-contract.**

(6) In the event that the Nominated Sub-contractor shall be in breach of the sub-contract which breach causes the Contractor to be in breach of contract the Employer shall not enforce any award of any arbitrator or judgment which he may obtain against the Contractor in respect of such breach of contract except to the extent that the Contractor may have been able to recover the amount thereof from the Sub-contractor. Provided always that if the Contractor shall not comply with Clause 59B (6) the Employer may enforce any such award or judgment in full.

**Forfeiture of Sub-contract.**

**59B.** (1) Subject to Clause 59A(2)(c) the Contractor shall in every sub-contract with a Nominated Sub-contractor incorporate provisions equivalent to those provided in Clause 63 and such provisions are hereinafter referred to as " the Forfeiture Clause ".

**Termination of Sub-contract.**

(2) If any event arises which in the opinion of the Contractor would entitle the Contractor to exercise his right under the Forfeiture Clause (or in the event that there shall be no Forfeiture Clause in the sub-contract his right to treat the sub-contract as repudiated by the Nominated Sub-contractor) he shall at once notify the Engineer in writing and if he desires to exercise such right by such notice seek the Employer's consent to his so doing. The Engineer shall by notice in writing to the Contractor inform him whether or not the Employer does so consent and if the Engineer does not give notice withholding consent within 7 days of receipt of the Contractor's notice the Employer shall be deemed to have consented to the exercise of the said right. If notice is given by the Contractor to the Engineer under this sub-clause and has not been withdrawn then notwithstanding that the Contractor has not sought the Employer's consent as aforesaid the Engineer may with the Employer's consent direct the Contractor to give notice to the Nominated Sub-contractor expelling the Nominated Sub-contractor from the sub-contract Works pursuant to the Forfeiture Clause or rescinding the sub-contract as the case may be. Any such notice given to the Nominated Sub-contractor is hereinafter referred to as a notice enforcing forfeiture of the sub-contract.

**Engineer's Action upon Termination.**

(3) If the Contractor shall give a notice enforcing forfeiture of the sub-contract whether under and in accordance with the Forfeiture Clause in the sub-contract or in purported exercise of his right to treat the sub-contract as repudiated the Engineer shall do any one or more of the things described in paragraphs (a) (b) and (d) of Clause 59A(2).

(b)   by order under Clause 51 vary the Works or the work goods materials or services in question or

(c)   by order under Clause 51 omit any or any part of such works goods materials or services so that they may be provided by workmen contractors or suppliers employed by the Employer either

    (i)   concurrently with the Works (in which case Clause 31 shall apply) or

    (ii)   at some other date

and in either case there shall nevertheless be included in the Contract Price such sum (if any) in respect of the Contractor's charges and profit being a percentage of the estimated value of such omission as would have been payable had there been no such omission and the value thereof had been that estimated in the Bill of Quantities or inserted in the Appendix to the Form of Tender as the case may be or

(d)   instruct the Contractor to secure a sub-contractor of his own choice and to submit a quotation for the work goods materials or services in question to be so performed or provided for the Engineer's consideration and action or

(e)   invite the Contractor himself to execute or supply the work goods materials or services in question under Clause 58(1)(a) or Clause 58(2)(b) or on a daywork basis as the case may be.

*This Clause now not only governs the action of the Engineer in the event that the Contractor has a valid objection to a sub-contractor nominated by the Engineer but also covers the situation where a re-nomination is necessary following a valid termination of a Nominated Sub-Contract. The Clause is substantially as previous Clause 59A(2) but omitting sub-clause (2)(c) so that there is no provision for the employment of a Nominated Sub-Contractor on terms that are in conflict with the provisions of Clause 59(1). Sub-clause 59(2)(d) has been added to provide specifically an option for the Contractor himself to obtain a quotation from a direct sub-contractor for carrying out the work.*

*Previous Clause 59A(3) has been omitted.*

**Contractor responsible for Nominated Sub-contractors**

(3)   Except as otherwise provided in Clause 58 (3) the Contractor shall be as responsible for the work executed or goods materials or services supplied by a Nominated Sub-contractor employed by him as if he had himself executed such work or supplied such goods materials or services.

**Nominated Sub-contractor's default**

(4)   (a)   If any event arises which in the opinion of the Contractor justifies the exercise of his right under the Forfeiture Clause to terminate the sub-contract or to treat the sub-contract as repudiated by the Nominated Sub-contractor he shall at once notify the Engineer in writing.

**Termination of Sub-contract**

(b)   With the consent in writing of the Engineer the Contractor may give notice to the Nominated Sub-contractor expelling him from the Sub-contract works pursuant to the Forfeiture Clause or rescinding the Sub-contract as the case may be. If however the Engineer's consent is withheld the Contractor shall be entitled to appropriate instructions under Clause 13.

**Engineer's action upon termination**

(c)   In the event that the Nominated Sub-contractor is expelled from the Sub-contract works the Engineer shall at once take such action as is required under sub-clause (2) of this Clause.

**Delay and Extra Cost.**

(4) If a notice enforcing forfeiture of the sub-contract shall have been given with the consent of the Employer or by the direction of the Engineer or if it shall have been given without the Employer's consent in circumstances which entitled the Contractor to give such a notice:—

(a) there shall be included in the Contract Price:—

  (i) the value determined in accordance with Clause 52 of any work the Contractor may have executed or goods or materials he may have provided subsequent to the forfeiture taking effect and pursuant to the Engineer's direction;

  (ii) such amount calculated in accordance with paragraph (a) of Clause 59A(5) as may be due in respect of any work goods materials or services provided by an alternative Nominated Sub-contractor together with reasonable sums for labours and for all other charges and profit as may be determined by the Engineer;

  (iii) any such amount as may be due in respect of the forfeited sub-contract in accordance with Clause 59A(5);

(b) the Engineer shall take any delay to the completion of the Works consequent upon the forfeiture into account in determining any extension of time to which the Contractor is entitled under Clause 44 and the Contractor shall subject to Clause 52(4) be paid in accordance with Clause 60 the amount of any additional cost which he may have necessarily and properly incurred as a result of such delay;

(c) the Employer shall subject to Clause 60(7) be entitled to recover from the Contractor upon the certificate of the Engineer issued in accordance with Clause 60(3):—

  (i) the amount by which the total sum to be included in the Contract Price pursuant to paragraphs (a) and (b) of this sub-clause exceeds the sum which would but for the forfeiture have been included in the Contract Price in respect of work materials goods and services done supplied or performed under the forfeited sub-contract;

  (ii) all such other loss expense and damage as the Employer may have suffered in consequence of the breach of the sub-contract;

all of which are hereinafter collectively called " the Employer's loss ".

Provided always that if the Contractor shall show that despite his having complied with sub-clause (6) of this Clause he has been unable to recover the whole or any part of the Employer's loss from the Sub-contractor the Employer shall allow or (if he has already recovered the same from the Contractor) shall repay to the Contractor so much of the Employer's loss as was irrecoverable from the Sub-contractor except and to the extent that the same was irrecoverable by reason of some breach of the sub-contract or other default towards the Sub-contractor by the Contractor or except to the extent that any act or default of the Contractor may have caused or contributed to any of the Employer's loss. Any such repayment by the Employer shall carry interest at the rate stipulated in Clause 60(6) from the date of the recovery by the Employer from the Contractor of the sum repaid.

**Termination Without Consent.**

(5) If notice enforcing forfeiture of the sub-contract shall have been given without the consent of the Employer and in circumstances which did not entitle the Contractor to give such a notice:—

(a) there shall be included in the Contract Price in respect of the whole of the work covered by the Nominated Sub-contract only the amount that would have been payable to the Nominated Sub-contractor on due completion of the sub-contract had it not been terminated;

(b) the Contractor shall not be entitled to any extension of time because of such termination nor to any additional expense incurred as a result of the work having been carried out and completed otherwise than by the said Sub-contractor;

(c) the Employer shall be entitled to recover from the Contractor any additional expense he may incur beyond that which he would have incurred had the sub-contract not been terminated.

**Recovery of Employer's Loss.**

(6) The Contractor shall take all necessary steps and proceedings as may be required by the Employer to enforce the provisions of the sub-contract and/or all other rights and/or remedies available to him so as to recover the Employer's loss from the Sub-contractor. Except in the case where notice enforcing forfeiture of the sub-contract shall have been given without the consent of the Employer and in circumstances which did not entitle the Contractor to give such a notice the Employer shall pay to the Contractor so much of the reasonable costs and expenses of such steps and proceedings as are irrecoverable from the Sub-contractor provided that if the Contractor shall seek to recover by the same steps and proceedings any loss damage or expense additional to the Employer's loss the said irrecoverable costs and expenses shall be borne by the Contractor and the Employer in such proportions as may be fair in all the circumstances.

**Payment to Nominated Sub-contractors.**

59C. Before issuing any certificate under Clause 60 the Engineer shall be entitled to demand from the Contractor reasonable proof that all sums (less retentions provided for in the sub-contract) included in previous certificates in respect of the work executed or goods or materials or services supplied by Nominated Sub-contractors have been paid to the Nominated Sub-contractors or discharged by the Contractor in default whereof unless the Contractor shall:—

**Delay and extra expense**

(d)  Having with the Engineer's consent terminated the Nominated Sub-contract the Contractor shall take all necessary steps and proceedings as are available to him to recover all additional expenses that are incurred from the Sub-contractor or under the security provided pursuant to sub-clause (1)(d) of this Clause. Such expenses shall include any additional expenses incurred by the Employer as a result of the termination.

**Reimbursement of Contractor's loss**

(e)  If and to the extent that the Contractor fails to recover all his reasonable expenses of completing the Sub-contract works and all his proper additional expenses arising from the termination the Employer will reimburse the Contractor his unrecovered expenses.

*New Clause to cover the procedure that must be followed in the event of the Nominated Sub-Contractor's default. The Sub-Contract can be terminated only with the consent in writing of the Engineer.*

*Previous Clause 59B has been omitted now being covered by Clause 59(4).*

**Provisions for payment**

(5)  For all work executed or goods materials or services supplied by Nominated Sub-contractors there shall be included in the Contract Price

(a)  the actual price paid or due to be paid by the Contractor in accordance with the terms of the sub-contract (unless and to the extent that any such payment is the result of a default of the Contractor) net of all trade and other discounts rebates and allowances other than any discount obtainable by the Contractor for prompt payment

(b)  the sum (if any) provided in the Bill of Quantitites for labours in connection therewith and

(c)  in respect of all other charges and profit a sum being a percentage of the actual price paid or due to be paid calculated (where provision has been made in the Bill of Quantities for a rate to be set against the relevant item of prime cost) at the rate inserted by the Contractor against that item or (where no such provision has been made) at the rate inserted by the Contractor in the Appendix to the Form of Tender as the percentage for adjustment of sums set against Prime Cost Items.

**Production of vouchers etc.**

(6)  The Contractor shall when required by the Engineer produce all quotations invoices vouchers sub-contract documents accounts and receipts in connection with expenditure in respect of work carried out by all Nominated Sub-contractors.

**Payment to Nominated Sub-contractors**

(7)  Before issuing any certificate under Clause 60 the Engineer shall be entitled to demand from the Contractor reasonable proof that all sums (less retentions provided for in the Sub-contract) included in previous certificates in respect of the work executed or goods or materials or services supplied by Nominated Sub-contractors have been paid to the Nominated Sub-contractors or discharged by the Contractor in default whereof unless the Contractor shall

(a)  give details to the Engineer in writing of any reasonable cause he may have for withholding or refusing to make such payment and

(b)  produce to the Engineer reasonable proof that he has so informed such Nominated Sub-contractor in writing

(a) give details to the Engineer in writing of any reasonable cause he may have for withholding or refusing to make such payment; and

(b) produce to the Engineer reasonable proof that he has so informed such Nominated Sub-contractor in writing;

the Employer shall be entitled to pay to such Nominated Sub-contractor direct upon the certification of the Engineer all payments (less retentions provided for in the sub-contract) which the Contractor has failed to make to such Nominated Sub-contractor and to deduct by way of set-off the amount so paid by the Employer from any sums due or which become due from the Employer to the Contractor. Provided always that where the Engineer has certified and the Employer has paid direct as aforesaid the Engineer shall in issuing any further certificate in favour of the Contractor deduct from the amount thereof the amount so paid direct as aforesaid but shall not withhold or delay the issue of the certificate itself when due to be issued under the terms of the Contract.

## CERTIFICATES AND PAYMENT

**Monthly Statements.**

60. (1) The Contractor shall submit to the Engineer after the end of each month a statement (in such form if any as may be prescribed in the Specification) showing:—

(a) the estimated contract value of the Permanent Works executed up to the end of that month;

(b) a list of any goods or materials delivered to the Site for but not yet incorporated in the Permanent Works and their value;

(c) a list of any goods or materials listed in the Appendix to the Form of Tender which have not yet been delivered to the Site but of which the property has vested in the Employer pursuant to Clause 54 and their value;

(d) the estimated amounts to which the Contractor considers himself entitled in connection with all other matters for which provision is made under the Contract including any Temporary Works or Constructional Plant for which separate amounts are included in the Bill of Quantities;

unless in the opinion of the Contractor such values and amounts together will not justify the issue of an interim certificate.

Amounts payable in respect of Nominated Sub-contractors are to be listed separately.

**Monthly Payments.**

(2) Within 28 days of the date of delivery to the Engineer or Engineer's Representative in accordance with sub-clause (1) of this Clause of the Contractor's monthly statement the Engineer shall certify and the Employer shall pay to the Contractor (after deducting any previous payments on account):—

(a) the amount which in the opinion of the Engineer on the basis of the monthly statement is due to the Contractor on account of sub-clause (1)(a) and (d) of this Clause less a retention as provided in sub-clause (4) of this Clause;

(b) such amounts (if any) as the Engineer may consider proper (but in no case exceeding the percentage of the value stated in the Appendix to the Form of Tender) in respect of (b) and (c) of sub-clause (1) of this Clause which amounts shall not be subject to a retention under sub-clause (4) of this Clause.

The amounts certified in respect of Nominated Sub-contracts shall be shown separately in the certificate. The Engineer shall not be bound to issue an interim certificate for a sum less than that named in the Appendix to the Form of Tender.

the Employer shall be entitled to pay to such Nominated Sub-contractor direct upon the certification of the Engineer all payments (less retentions provided for in the Sub-contract) which the Contractor has failed to make to such Nominated Sub-contractor and to deduct by way of set-off the amount so paid by the Employer from any sums due or which become due from the Employer to the Contractor. Provided always that where the Engineer has certified and the Employer has made direct payment to the Nominated Sub-contractor the Engineer shall in issuing any further certificate in favour of the Contractor deduct from the amount thereof the amount so paid but shall not withhold or delay the issue of the certificate itself when due to be issued under the terms of the Contract.

*As previous Clause 59C.*

## CERTIFICATES AND PAYMENT

**Monthly statements** **60** (1)   The Contractor shall submit to the Engineer at monthly intervals a statement (in such form if any as may be prescribed in the Specification) showing

(a)   the estimated contract value of the Permanent Works executed up to the end of that month

(b)   a list of any goods or materials delivered to the Site for but not yet incorporated in the Permanent Works and their value

(c)   a list of any of those goods or materials identified in the Appendix to the Form of Tender which have not yet been delivered to the Site but of which the property has vested in the Employer pursuant to Clause 54 and their value and

(d)   the estimated amounts to which the Contractor considers himself entitled in connection with all other matters for which provision is made under the Contract including any Temporary Works or Contractor's Equipment for which separate amounts are included in the Bill of Quantities

unless in the opinion of the Contractor such values and amounts together will not justify the issue of an interim certificate.

Amounts payable in respect of Nominated Sub-contracts are to be listed separately.

*As previous Clause 60(1) except that statements are to be submitted at monthly intervals instead of at the end of each month.*

**Monthly payments** (2)   Within 28 days of the date of delivery to the Engineer or Engineer's Representative in accordance with sub-clause (1) of this Clause of the Contractor's monthly statement the Engineer shall certify and the Employer shall pay to the Contractor (after deducting any previous payments on account)

(a)   the amount which in the opinion of the Engineer on the basis of the monthly statement is due to the Contractor on account of sub-clauses (1)(a) and (1)(d) of this Clause less a retention as provided in sub-clause (5) of this Clause and

(b)   such amounts (if any) as the Engineer may consider proper (but in no case exceeding the percentage of the value stated in the Appendix to the Form of Tender) in respect of sub-clauses (1)(b) and (1)(c) of this Clause.

The amounts certified in respect of Nominated Sub-contracts shall be shown separately in the certificate.

**Final Account.** (3) Not later than 3 months after the date of the Maintenance Certificate the Contractor shall submit to the Engineer a statement of final account and supporting documentation showing in detail the value in accordance with the Contract of the work done in accordance with the Contract together with all further sums which the Contractor considers to be due to him under the Contract up to the date of the Maintenance Certificate. Within 3 months after receipt of this final account and of all information reasonably required for its verification the Engineer shall issue a final certificate stating the amount which in his opinion is finally due under the Contract up to the date of the Maintenance Certificate and after giving credit to the Employer for all amounts previously paid by the Employer and for all sums to which the Employer is entitled under the Contract up to the date of the Maintenance Certificate the balance if any due from the Employer to the Contractor or from the Contractor to the Employer as the case may be. Such balance shall subject to Clause 47 be paid to or by the Contractor as the case may require within 28 days of the date of the certificate.

**Retention.** (4) The retention to be made pursuant to sub-clause (2)(a) of this Clause shall be a sum equal to 5 per cent of the amount due to the Contractor until a reserve shall have accumulated in the hand of the Employer up to the following limits:—

(a) where the Tender Total does not exceed £50,000 5 per cent of the Tender Total but not exceeding £1,500; or

(b) where the Tender Total exceeds £50,000 3 per cent of the Tender Total;

except that the limit shall be reduced by the amount of any payment that shall have been made pursuant to sub-clause (5) of this Clause.

**Payment of Retention Money.** (5) (a) If the Engineer shall issue a Certificate of Completion in respect of any Section or part of the Works pursuant to Clause 48(2) or (3) there shall become due on the date of issue of such certificate and shall be paid to the Contractor within 14 days thereof a sum equal to 1½ per cent of the amount due to the Contractor at that date in respect of such Section or part as certified for payment pursuant to sub-clause (2) of this Clause provided that any sum or sums paid under this sub-clause shall not exceed in aggregate one half of the retention money deducted in accordance with sub-clause (2)(a) of this Clause from the payments made to the Contractor at the date of issue by the Engineer of the aforesaid Certificate of Completion.

(b) One half of the retention money less any sums paid pursuant to sub-clause (5)(a) of this Clause shall be paid to the Contractor within 14 days after the date on which the Engineer shall have issued a Certificate of Completion for the whole of the Works pursuant to Clause 48(1).

(c) The other half of the retention money shall be paid to the Contractor within 14 days after the expiration of the Period of Maintenance notwithstanding that at such time there may be outstanding claims by the Contractor against the Employer. Provided always that if at such time there shall remain to be executed by the Contractor any outstanding work referred to under Clause 48 or any works ordered during such period pursuant to Clauses 49 and 50 the Employer shall be entitled to withhold payment until the completion of such works of so much of the second half of retention money as shall in the opinion of the Engineer represent the cost of the works so remaining to be executed.

Provided further that in the event of different maintenance periods having become applicable to different Sections or parts of the Works pursuant to Clause 48 the expression " expiration of the Period of Maintenance " shall for the purposes of this sub-clause be deemed to mean the expiration of the latest of such periods.

**Minimum amount of certificate**

(3) Until the whole of the Works has been certified as substantially complete in accordance with Clause 48 the Engineer shall not be bound to issue an interim certificate for a sum less than that stated in the Appendix to the Form of Tender but thereafter he shall be bound to do so and the certification and payment of amounts due to the Contractor shall be in accordance with the time limits contained in this Clause.

*This Clause is the last sentence of previous Clause 60(2) but has been extended to make it clear that minimum certificates apply only up to the date of substantial completion of the whole of the Works.*

**Final account**

(4) Not later than 3 months after the date of the Defects Correction Certificate the Contractor shall submit to the Engineer a statement of final account and supporting documentation showing in detail the value in accordance with the Contract of the Works executed together with all further sums which the Contractor considers to be due to him under the Contract up to the date of the Defects Correction Certificate.

Within 3 months after receipt of this final account and of all information reasonably required for its verification the Engineer shall issue a certificate stating the amount which in his opinion is finally due under the Contract from the Employer to the Contractor or from the Contractor to the Employer as the case may be up to the date of the Defects Correction Certificate and after giving credit to the Employer for all amounts previously paid by the Employer and for all sums to which the Employer is entitled under the Contract.

Such amount shall subject to Clause 47 be paid to or by the Contractor as the case may require within 28 days of the date of the certificate.

**Retention**

(5) The retention to be made pursuant to sub-clause (2)(a) of this Clause shall be the difference between

(a) an amount calculated at the rate indicated in and up to the limit set out in the Appendix to the Form of Tender upon the amount due to the Contractor on account of sub-clauses (1)(a) and (1)(d) of this Clause and

(b) any payment which shall have become due under sub-clause (6) of this Clause.

*Revised Clause (previously Clause 60(4)) referring to the Appendix to the Form of Tender for the rate and limit of retention.*

**Payment of retention**

(6) (a) Upon the issue of a Certificate of Substantial Completion in respect of any Section or part of the Works there shall become due to the Contractor one half of such proportion of the retention money deductible to date under sub-clause (5)(a) of this Clause as the value of the Section or part bears to the value of the whole of the Works completed to date as certified under sub-clause (2)(a) of this Clause and such amount shall be added to the amount next certified as due to the Contractor under sub-clause (2) of this Clause.

The total of the amounts released shall in no event exceed one half of the limit of retention set out in the Appendix to the Form of Tender.

(b) Upon issue of the Certificate of Substantial Completion in respect of the whole of the Works there shall become due to the Contractor one half of the retention money calculated in accordance with sub-clause (5)(a) of this Clause. The amount so due (or the balance thereof over and above such payments already made pursuant to sub-clause (6)(a) of this Clause) shall be paid within 14 days of the issue of the said Certificate.

**Interest on Overdue Payments.**

(6) In the event of failure by the Engineer to certify or the Employer to make payment in accordance with sub-clauses (2) (3) and (5) of this Clause the Employer shall pay to the Contractor interest upon any payment overdue thereunder at a rate per annum equivalent to 2 per cent plus the minimum rate at which the Bank of England will lend to a discount house having access to the Discount Office of the Bank current on the date upon which such payment first becomes overdue. In the event of any variation in the said Minimum Lending Rate being announced whilst such payment remains overdue the interest payable to the Contractor for the period that such payment remains overdue shall be correspondingly varied from the date of each such variation.

**Correction and Withholding of Certificates.**

(7) The Engineer shall have power to omit from any certificate the value of any work done goods or materials supplied or services rendered with which he may for the time being be dissatisfied and for that purpose or for any other reason which to him may seem proper may by any certificate delete correct or modify any sum previously certified by him.

Provided always that:—

(a) the Engineer shall not in any interim certificate delete or reduce any sum previously certified in respect of work done goods or materials supplied or services rendered by a Nominated Sub-contractor if the Contractor shall have already paid or be bound to pay that sum to the Nominated Sub-contractor;

(b) if the Engineer in the final certificate shall delete or reduce any sum previously certified in respect of work done goods or materials supplied or services rendered by a Nominated Sub-contractor which sum shall have been already paid by the Contractor to the Nominated Sub-contractor the Employer shall reimburse to the Contractor the amount of any sum overpaid by the Contractor to the Sub-contractor in accordance with the certificates issued under sub-clause (2) of this Clause which the Contractor despite compliance with Clause 59B(6) shall be unable to recover from the Nominated Sub-contractor together with interest thereon at the rate stated in Clause 60(6) from 28 days after the date of the final certificate issued under sub-clause (3) of this Clause until the date of such reimbursement.

(c)  Upon the expiry of the Defects Correction Period or if more than one the last of such periods the remainder of the retention money shall be paid to the Contractor within 14 days notwithstanding that at that time there may be outstanding claims by the Contractor against the Employer.

Provided that if at that time there remains to be executed by the Contractor any outstanding work referred to under Clause 48 or any work ordered pursuant to Clauses 49 or 50 the Employer may withhold payment until the completion of such work of so much of the said remainder as shall in the opinion of the Engineer represent the cost of the work remaining to be executed.

*Substantially as previous Clause 60(5). Reference is now made to half of the relevant proportion of the retention money deducted instead of 1.5% of the amount due to the Contractor. Retention released when Sections or parts of the Works are completed to be in proportion to value and to be included in certificate next issued.*

**Interest on overdue payments**

(7)  In the event of

(a)  failure by the Engineer to certify or the Employer to make payment in accordance with sub-clauses (2) (4) or (6) of this Clause or

(b)  any finding of an arbitrator to such effect

the Employer shall pay to the Contractor interest compounded monthly for each day on which any payment is overdue or which should have been certified and paid at a rate equivalent to 2% per annum above the base lending rate of the bank specified in the Appendix to the Form of Tender. If in an arbitration pursuant to Clause 66 the arbitrator holds that any sum or additional sum should have been certified by a particular date in accordance with the aforementioned sub-clauses but was not so certified this shall be regarded for the purposes of this sub-clause as a failure to certify such sum or additional sum. Such sum or additional sum shall be regarded as overdue for payment 28 days after the date by which the arbitrator holds that the Engineer should have certified the sum or if no such date is identified by the arbitrator shall be regarded as overdue for payment from the date of the Certificate of Substantial Completion for the whole of the Works.

*The previous Clause 60(6) has been expanded to make it clear that interest is payable for each day a payment is overdue and that the interest is to be compounded monthly so that interest is added each month to the interest already due to be paid on an overdue payment. The wording of the Clause has also been revised to refer to the bank specified in the Appendix to the Form of Tender. An addition has been made so that the English and Scottish procedures for the award of interest on Certificates corrected by an Arbitrator are the same.*

**Correction and withholding of certificates**

(8)  The Engineer shall have power to omit from any certificate the value of any work done goods or materials supplied or services rendered with which he may for the time being be dissatisfied and for that purpose or for any other reason which to him may seem proper may by any certificate delete correct or modify any sum previously certified by him. Provided that

(a)  the Engineer shall not in any interim certificate delete or reduce any sum previously certified in respect of work done goods or materials supplied or services rendered by a Nominated Sub-contractor if the Contractor shall have already paid or be bound to pay that sum to the Nominated Sub-contractor and

**Copy Certificate for Contractor.**

(8) Every certificate issued by the Engineer pursuant to this Clause shall be sent to the Employer and at the same time a copy thereof shall be sent to the Contractor.

**Maintenance Certificate.**

**61.** (1) Upon the expiration of the Period of Maintenance or where there is more than one such period upon the expiration of the latest period and when all outstanding work referred to under Clause 48 and all work of repair amendment reconstruction rectification and making good of defects imperfections shrinkages and other faults referred to under Clauses 49 and 50 shall have been completed the Engineer shall issue to the Employer (with a copy to the Contractor) a Maintenance Certificate stating the date on which the Contractor shall have completed his obligations to construct complete and maintain the Works to the Engineer's satisfaction.

**Unfulfilled Obligations.**

(2) The issue of the Maintenance Certificate shall not be taken as relieving either the Contractor or the Employer from any liability the one towards the other arising out of or in any way connected with the performance of their respective obligations under the Contract.

## REMEDIES AND POWERS

**Urgent Repairs.**

**62.** If by reason of any accident or failure or other event occurring to in or in connection with the Works or any part thereof either during the execution of the Works or during the Period of Maintenance any remedial or other work or repair shall in the opinion of the Engineer be urgently necessary and the Contractor is unable or unwilling at once to do such work or repair the Employer may by his own or other workmen do such work or repair as the Engineer may consider necessary. If the work or repair so done by the Employer is work which in the opinion of the Engineer the Contractor was liable to do at his own expense under the Contract all costs and charges properly incurred by the Employer in so doing shall on demand be paid by the Contractor to the Employer or may be deducted by the Employer from any monies due or which may become due to the Contractor. Provided always that the Engineer shall as soon after the occurrence of any such emergency as may be reasonably practicable notify the Contractor thereof in writing.

(b)  if the Engineer in the final certificate shall delete or reduce any sum previously certified in respect of work done goods or materials supplied or services rendered by a Nominated Sub-contractor which sum shall have been already paid by the Contractor to the Nominated Sub-contractor the Employer shall reimburse to the Contractor the amount of any sum overpaid by the Contractor to the Sub-contractor in accordance with the certificates issued under sub-clause (2) of this Clause which the Contractor shall be unable to recover from the Nominated Sub-contractor together with interest thereon at the rate stated in sub-clause (7) of this Clause from 28 days after the date of the final certificate issued under sub-clause (4) of this Clause until the date of such reimbursement.

**Copy of certificate for Contractor**

(9)  Every certificate issued by the Engineer pursuant to this Clause shall be sent to the Employer and at the same time copied to the Contractor with such detailed explanation as may be necessary.

**Payment advice**

(10)  Where a payment made in accordance with sub-clause (2) of this Clause differs in any respect from the amount certified by the Engineer the Employer shall notify the Contractor forthwith with full details showing how the amount being paid has been calculated.

*Under this new Clause the Employer has to give a detailed explanation if the amount of a payment differs in any respect from the amount certified by the Engineer.*

**Defects Correction Certificate**

61  (1)  Upon the expiry of the Defects Correction Period or where there is more than one such period upon the expiration of the last of such periods and when all outstanding work referred to under Clause 48 and all work of repair amendment reconstruction rectification and making good of defects imperfections shrinkages and other faults referred to under Clauses 49 and 50 shall have been completed the Engineer shall issue to the Employer (with a copy to the Contractor) a Defects Correction Certificate stating the date on which the Contractor shall have completed his obligations to construct and complete the Works to the Engineer's satisfaction.

**Unfulfilled obligations**

(2)  The issue of the Defects Correction Certificate shall not be taken as relieving either the Contractor or the Employer from any liability the one towards the other arising out of or in any way connected with the performance of their respective obligations under the Contract.

## REMEDIES AND POWERS

**Urgent repairs**

62  If by reason of any accident or failure or other event occurring to in or in connection with the Works or any part thereof either during the execution of the Works or during the Defects Correction Period any remedial or other work or repair shall in the opinion of the Engineer or the Engineer's Representative be urgently necessary and the Contractor is unable or unwilling at once to do such work or repair the Employer may by his own or other workpeople do such work or repair. If the work or repair so done by the Employer is work which in the opinion of the Engineer the Contractor was liable to do at his own expense under the Contract all costs and charges properly incurred by the Employer in so doing shall on demand be paid by the Contractor to the Employer or may be deducted by the Employer from any monies due or which may become due to the Contractor. Provided that the Engineer shall as soon after the occurrence of any such emergency as may be reasonably practicable notify the Contractor thereof in writing.

*Substantially as previous Clause 62 but with authority also given to the Engineer's Representative.*

**Forfeiture.**

**63.** (1) If the Contractor shall become bankrupt or have a receiving order made against him or shall present his petition in bankruptcy or shall make an arrangement with or assignment in favour of his creditors or shall agree to carry out the Contract under a committee of inspection of his creditors or (being a corporation) shall go into liquidation (other than a voluntary liquidation for the purposes of amalgamation or reconstruction) or if the Contractor shall assign the Contract without the consent in writing of the Employer first obtained or shall have an execution levied on his goods or if the Engineer shall certify in writing to the Employer that in his opinion the Contractor:—

(a) has abandoned the Contract; or

(b) without reasonable excuse has failed to commence the Works in accordance with Clause 41 or has suspended the progress of the Works for 14 days after receiving from the Engineer written notice to proceed; or

(c) has failed to remove goods or materials from the Site or to pull down and replace work for 14 days after receiving from the Engineer written notice that the said goods materials or work have been condemned and rejected by the Engineer; or

(d) despite previous warning by the Engineer in writing is failing to proceed with the Works with due diligence or is otherwise persistently or fundamentally in breach of his obligations under the Contract; or

(e) has to the detriment of good workmanship or in defiance of the Engineer's instruction to the contrary sub-let any part of the Contract;

then the Employer may after giving 7 days' notice in writing to the Contractor enter upon the Site and the Works and expel the Contractor therefrom without thereby avoiding the Contract or releasing the Contractor from any of his obligations or liabilities under the Contract or affecting the rights and powers conferred on the Employer or the Engineer by the Contract and may himself complete the Works or may employ any other contractor to complete the Works and the Employer or such other contractor may use for such completion so much of the Constructional Plant Temporary Works goods and materials which have been deemed to become the property of the Employer under Clauses 53 and 54 as he or they may think proper and the Employer may at any time sell any of the said Constructional Plant Temporary Works and unused goods and materials and apply the proceeds of sale in or towards the satisfaction of any sums due or which may become due to him from the Contractor under the Contract.

**Determination of the Contractor's employment**

**63** (1) If

    (a) the Contractor shall be in default in that he

        (i) becomes bankrupt or has a receiving order or administration order made against him or presents his petition in bankruptcy or makes an arrangement with or assignment in favour of his creditors or agrees to carry out the Contract under a committee of inspection of his creditors or (being a corporation) goes into liquidation (other than a voluntary liquidation for the purposes of amalgamation or reconstruction) or

        (ii) assigns the Contract without the consent in writing of the Employer first obtained or

        (iii) has an execution levied on his goods which is not stayed or discharged within 28 days

or

    (b) the Engineer certifies in writing to the Employer with a copy to the Contractor that in his opinion the Contractor

        (i) has abandoned the Contract or

        (ii) without reasonable excuse has failed to commence the Works in accordance with Clause 41 or has suspended the progress of the Works for 14 days after receiving from the Engineer written notice to proceed or

        (iii) has failed to remove goods or materials from the Site or to pull down and replace work for 14 days after recieving from the Engineer written notice that the said goods materials or work have been condemned and rejected by the Engineer or

        (iv) despite previous warnings by the Engineer in writing is failing to proceed with the Works with due diligence or is otherwise persistently or fundamentally in breach of his obligations under Contract

then the Employer may after giving 7 days' notice in writing to the Contractor specifying the default enter upon the Site and the Works and expel the Contractor therefrom without thereby avoiding the Contract or releasing the Contractor from any of his obligations or liabilities under the Contract. Provided that the Employer may extend the period of notice to give the Contractor opportunity to remedy the default.

Where a notice of determination is given pursuant to this sub-clause it shall be given as soon as is reasonably possible after receipt of the Engineer's certificate.

*The defaults listed in sub-clause (a) now include the Contractor having had an administration order made against him.*

**Completing the Works**

(2) Where the Employer has entered upon the Site and the Works as hereinbefore provided he may himself complete the Works or may employ any other contractor to complete the Works and the Employer or such other contractor may use for such completion so much of the Contractor's Equipment Temporary Works goods and materials which have been deemed to become the property of the Employer under Clauses 53 and 54 as he or they may think proper and the Employer may at any time sell any of the said Contractor's Equipment Temporary Works and unused goods and materials and apply the proceeds of sale in or towards the satisfaction of any sums due or which may become due to him from the Contractor under the Contract.

**Assignment to Employer.**

(2)   By the said notice or by further notice in writing within 14 days of the date thereof the Engineer may require the Contractor to assign to the Employer and if so required the Contractor shall forthwith assign to the Employer the benefit of any agreement for the supply of any goods or materials and/or for the execution of any work for the purposes of this Contract which the Contractor may have entered into.

**Valuation at Date of Forfeiture.**

(3)   The Engineer shall as soon as may be practicable after any such entry and expulsion by the Employer fix and determine *ex parte* or by or after reference to the parties or after such investigation or enquiries as he may think fit to make or institute and shall certify what amount (if any) had at the time of such entry and expulsion been reasonably earned by or would reasonably accrue to the Contractor in respect of work then actually done by him under the Contract and what was the value of any unused or partially used goods and materials any Constructional Plant and any Temporary Works which have been deemed to become the property of the Employer under Clauses 53 and 54.

**Payment after Forfeiture.**

(4)   If the Employer shall enter and expel the Contractor under this Clause he shall not be liable to pay to the Contractor any money on account of the Contract until the expiration of the Period of Maintenance and thereafter until the costs of completion and maintenance damages for delay in completion (if any) and all other expenses incurred by the Employer have been ascertained and the amount thereof certified by the Engineer.   The Contractor shall then be entitled to receive only such sum or sums (if any) as the Engineer may certify would have been due to him upon due completion by him after deducting the said amount.   But if such amount shall exceed the sum which would have been payable to the Contractor on due completion by him then the Contractor shall upon demand pay to the Employer the amount of such excess and it shall be deemed a debt due by the Contractor to the Employer and shall be recoverable accordingly.

## FRUSTRATION

**Payment in Event of Frustration.**

**64.**   In the event of the Contract being frustrated whether by war or by any other supervening event which may occur independently of the will of the parties the sum payable by the Employer to the Contractor in respect of the work executed shall be the same as that which would have been payable under Clause 65(5) if the Contract had been determined by the Employer under Clause 65.

## WAR CLAUSE

**Works to Continue for 28 Days on Outbreak of War.**

**65.**   (1)   If during the currency of the Contract there shall be an outbreak of war (whether war is declared or not) in which Great Britain shall be engaged on a scale involving general mobilisation of the armed forces of the Crown the Contractor shall for a period of 28 days reckoned from midnight on the date that the order for general mobilisation is given continue so far as is physically possible to execute the Works in accordance with the Contract.

**Assignment to Employer**

(3)  By the said notice or by further notice in writing within 7 days of the date of expiry thereof the Engineer may require the Contractor to assign to the Employer and if so required the Contractor shall forthwith assign to the Employer the benefit of any agreement for the supply of any goods or materials and/or for the execution of any work for the purposes of this Contract which the Contractor may have entered into.

**Payment after determination**

(4)  If the Employer enters and expels the Contractor under this Clause he shall not be liable to pay to the Contractor any money on account of the Contract until the expiration of the Defects Correction Period and thereafter until the costs of completion damages for delay in completion (if any) and all other expenses incurred by the Employer have been ascertained and the amount thereof certified by the Engineer.

The Contractor shall then be entitled to receive only such sum or sums (if any) as the Engineer may certify would have been due to him upon due completion by him after deducting the said amount. But if such amount shall exceed the sum which would have been payable to the Contractor on due completion by him then the Contractor shall upon demand pay to the Employer the amount of such excess and it shall be deemed a debt due by the Contractor to the Employer and shall be recoverable accordingly.

**Valuation at date of determination**

(5)  As soon as may be practicable after any such entry and expulsion by the Employer the Engineer shall fix and determine as at the time of such entry and expulsion

(a)  the amount (if any) which had been reasonably earned by or would reasonably accrue to the Contractor in respect of work actually done by him under the Contract and

(b)  the value of any unused or partially used goods and materials and any Contractor's Equipment and Temporary Works which had been deemed to become the property of the Employer under Clauses 53 and 54

and shall certify accordingly.

The said determination may be carried out ex parte or by or after reference to the parties or after such investigation or enquiry as the Engineer may think fit to make or institute.

## FRUSTRATION

**Payment in event of frustration**   64

In the event of the Contract being frustrated whether by war or by any other supervening event which may occur independently of the will of the parties the sum payable by the Employer to the Contractor in respect of the work executed shall be the same as that which would have been payable under Clause 65(5) if the Contract had been determined by the Employer under Clause 65.

## WAR CLAUSE

**Works to continue for 28 days on outbreak of war**   65

(1)  If during the currency of the Contract there shall be an outbreak of war (whether war is declared or not) in which Great Britain shall be engaged on a scale involving general mobilization of the armed forces of the Crown the Contractor shall for a period of 28 days reckoned from midnight on the date that the order for general mobilization is given continue so far as is physically possible to execute the Works in accordance with the Contract.

**Effect of Completion Within 28 Days.**

(2)   If at any time before the expiration of the said period of 28 days the Works shall have been completed or completed so far as to be usable all provisions of the Contract shall continue to have full force and effect save that:—

(a)   the Contractor shall in lieu of fulfilling his obligations under Clauses 49 and 50 be entitled at his option to allow against the sum due to him under the provisions hereof the cost (calculated at the prices ruling at the beginning of the said period of 28 days) as certified by the Engineer at the expiration of the Period of Maintenance of repair rectification and making good any work for the repair rectification or making good of which the Contractor would have been liable under the said Clauses had they continued to be applicable;

(b)   the Employer shall not be entitled at the expiration of the Period of Maintenance to withhold payment under Clause 60(5)(c) of the second half of the retention money or any part thereof except such sum as may be allowable by the Contractor under the provisions of the last preceding paragraph which sum may (without prejudice to any other mode of recovery thereof) be deducted by the Employer from such second half.

**Right of Employer to Determine Contract.**

(3)   If the Works shall not have been completed as aforesaid the Employer shall be entitled to determine the Contract (with the exception of this Clause and Clauses 66 and 68) by giving notice in writing to the Contractor at any time after the aforesaid period of 28 days has expired and upon such notice being given the Contract shall (except as above mentioned) forthwith determine but without prejudice to the claims of either party in respect of any antecedent breach thereof.

**Removal of Plant on Determination.**

(4)   If the Contract shall be determined under the provisions of the last preceding sub-clause the Contractor shall with all reasonable despatch remove from the Site all his Constructional Plant and shall give facilities to his sub-contractors to remove similarly all Constructional Plant belonging to them and in the event of any failure so to do the Employer shall have the like powers as are contained in Clause 53(8) in regard to failure to remove Constructional Plant on completion of the Works but subject to the same condition as is contained in Clause 53(9).

**Payment on Determination.**

(5)   If the Contract shall be determined as aforesaid the Contractor shall be paid by the Employer (insofar as such amounts or items shall not have been already covered by payment on account made to the Contractor) for all work executed prior to the date of determination at the rates and prices provided in the Contract and in addition:—

(a)   the amounts payable in respect of any preliminary items so far as the work or service comprised therein has been carried out or performed and a proper proportion as certified by the Engineer of any such items the work or service comprised in which has been partially carried out or performed;

(b)   the cost of materials or goods reasonably ordered for the Works which shall have been delivered to the Contractor or of which the Contractor is legally liable to accept delivery (such materials or goods becoming the property of the Employer upon such payment being made by him);

(c)   a sum to be certified by the Engineer being the amount of any expenditure reasonably incurred by the Contractor in the expectation of completing the whole of the Works in so far as such expenditure shall not have been covered by the payments in this sub-clause before mentioned;

(d)   any additional sum payable under sub-clause (6)(b)(c) and (d) of this Clause;

(e)   the reasonable cost of removal under sub-clause (4) of this Clause.

**Effect of completion within 28 days**

(2)   If at any time before the expiration of the said period of 28 days the Works shall have been completed or completed so far as to be usable all provisions of the Contract shall continue to have full force and effect save that

(a)   the Contractor shall in lieu of fulfilling his obligations under Clauses 49 and 50 be entitled at his option to allow against the sum due to him under the provisions hereof the cost (calculated at the prices ruling at the beginning of the said period of 28 days) as certified by the Engineer at the expiration of the Defects Correction Period of repair rectification and making good any work for the repair rectification or making good of which the Contractor would have been liable under the said Clauses had they continued to be applicable

(b)   the Employer shall not be entitled at the expiry of the Defects Correction Period to withold payment under Clause 60(5)(c) of the second half of the retention money or any part thereof except such sum as may be allowable by the Contractor under the provisions of the last preceding paragraph which sum may (without prejudice to any other mode of recovery thereof) be deducted by the Employer from such second half.

**Right of Employer to determine Contract**

(3)   If the Works shall not have been completed as aforesaid the Employer shall be entitled to determine the Contract (with the exception of this Clause and Clauses 66 and 68) by giving notice in writing to the Contractor at any time after the aforesaid period of 28 days has expired and upon such notice being given the Contract shall (except as above mentioned) forthwith determine but without prejudice to the claims of either party in respect of any antecedent breach thereof.

**Removal of Contractor's Equipment on determination**

(4)   If the Contract shall be determined under the provisions of the last preceding sub-clause the Contractor shall with all reasonable despatch remove from the Site all his Contractor's Equipment and shall give facilities to his sub-contractors to remove similarly all Contractor's Equipment belonging to them and in the event of any failure so to do the Employer shall have the like powers as are contained in Clause 53(3) in regard to failure to remove Contractor's Equipment on completion of the Works but subject to the same condition as is contained in Clause 53(3).

**Payment on determination**

(5)   If the Contract shall be determined as aforesaid the Contractor shall be paid by the Employer (insofar as such amounts or items shall not have been already covered by payment on account made to the Contractor) for all work executed prior to the date of determination at the rates and prices provided in the Contract and in addition

(a)   the amounts payable in respect of any preliminary items so far as the work or service comprised therein has been carried out or performed and a proper proportion as certified by the Engineer of any such items the work or service comprised in which has been partially carried out or performed

(b)   the cost of materials or goods reasonably ordered for the Works which have been delivered to the Contractor or of which the Contractor is legally liable to accept delivery (such materials or goods becoming the property of the Employer upon such payment being made by him)

**Provisions to Apply as from Outbreak of War.**

(6)   Whether the Contract shall be determined under the provisions of sub-clause (3) of this Clause or not the following provisions shall apply or be deemed to have applied as from the date of the said outbreak of war notwithstanding anything expressed in or implied by the other terms of the Contract *viz*:—

(a)   The Contractor shall be under no liability whatsoever whether by way of indemnity or otherwise for or in respect of damage to the Works or to property (other than property of the Contractor or property hired by him for the purposes of executing the Works) whether of the Employer or of third parties or for or in respect of injury or loss of life to persons which is the consequence whether direct or indirect of war hostilities (whether war has been declared or not) invasion act of the Queen's enemies civil war rebellion revolution-insurrection military or usurped power and the Employer shall indemnify the Contractor against all such liabilities and against all claims demands proceedings damages costs charges and expenses whatsoever arising thereout or in connection therewith.

(b)   If the Works shall sustain destruction or any damage by reason of any of the causes mentioned in the last preceding paragraph the Contractor shall nevertheless be entitled to payment for any part of the Works so destroyed or damaged and the Contractor shall be entitled to be paid by the Employer the cost of making good any such destruction or damage so far as may be required by the Engineer or as may be necessary for the completion of the Works on a cost basis plus such profit as the Engineer may certify to be reasonable.

(c)   In the event that the Contract includes the Contract Price Fluctuations Clause the terms of that Clause shall continue to apply but if subsequent to the outbreak of war the index figures therein referred to shall cease to be published or in the event that the contract shall not include a Price Fluctuations Clause in that form the following paragraph shall have effect:—

If under decision of the Civil Engineering Construction Conciliation Board or of any other body recognised as an appropriate body for regulating the rates of wages in any trade or industry other than the Civil Engineering Construction Industry to which Contractors undertaking works of civil engineering construction give effect by agreement or in practice or by reason of any Statute or Statutory Instrument there shall during the currency of the Contract be any increase or decrease in the wages or the rates of wages or in the allowances or rates of allowances (including allowances in respect of holidays) payable to or in respect of labour of any kind prevailing at the date of outbreak of war as then fixed by the said Board or such other body as aforesaid or by Statute or Statutory Instrument or any increase in the amount payable by the Contractor by virtue or in respect of any Scheme of State Insurance or if there shall be any increase or decrease in the cost prevailing at the date of the said outbreak of war of any materials consumable stores fuel or power (and whether for permanent or temporary works) which increase or increases decrease or decreases shall result in an increase or decrease of cost to the Contractor in carrying out the Works the net increase or decrease of cost shall form an addition or deduction as the case may be to or from the Contract Price and be paid to or allowed by the Contractor accordingly.

(d)   If the cost of the Works to the Contractor shall be increased or decreased by reason of the provisions of any Statute or Statutory Instrument or other Government or Local Government Order or Regulation becoming applicable to the Works after the date of the said outbreak of war or by reason of any trade or industrial agreement entered into after such date to which the Civil Engineering Construction Conciliation Board or any other body as aforesaid is party or gives effect or by reason of any amendment of whatsoever nature of the Working Rule Agreement of the said Board or of any other body as aforesaid or by reason of any other circumstance or thing attributable to or consequent on such outbreak of war such increase or decrease of cost as certified by the Engineer shall be reimbursed by the Employer to the Contractor or allowed by the Contractor as the case may be.

(c)   a sum to be certified by the Engineer being the amount of any expenditure reasonably incurred by the Contractor in the expectation of completing the whole of the Works in so far as such expenditure shall not have been covered by the payments in this sub-clause before mentioned

(d)   any additional sum payable under sub-clauses (6)(b)(c) and (d) of this Clause and

(e)   the reasonable cost of removal under sub-clause (4) of this Clause.

**Provisions to apply as from outbreak of war**

(6)   Whether the Contract shall be determined under the provisions of sub-clause (3) of this Clause or not the following provisions shall apply or be deemed to have applied as from the date of the said outbreak of war notwithstanding anything expressed in or implied by the other terms of the Contract viz

(a)   The Contractor shall be under no liability whatsoever by way of indemnity or otherwise for or in respect of damage to the Works or to property (other than property of the Contractor or property hired by him for the purposes of executing the Works) whether of the Employer or of third parties or for or in respect of injury or loss of life to persons which is the consequence whether direct or indirect of war hostilities (whether war has been declared or not) invasion act of the Queen's enemies civil war rebellion revolution insurrection military or usurped power and the Employer shall indemnify the Contractor against all such liabilities and against all claims demands proceedings damages costs charges and expenses whatsoever arising thereout or in connection therewith.

(b)   If the Works shall sustain destruction or any damage by reason of any of the causes mentioned in the last preceding paragraph the Contractor shall nevertheless be entitled to payment for any part of the Works so destroyed or damaged and the Contractor shall be entitled to be paid by the Employer the cost of making good any such destruction or damage so far as may be required by the Engineer or as may be necessary for the completion of the Works on a cost basis plus such profit as the Engineer may certify to be reasonable.

(c)   In the event that the Contract includes the Contract Price Fluctuations Clause the terms of that Clause shall continue to apply but if subsequent to the outbreak of war the index figures therein referred to shall cease to be published or in the event that the Contract shall not include a Contract Price Fluctuations Clause in that form the following paragraph shall have effect:

If under decision of the Civil Engineering Construction Conciliation Board or of any other body recognized as an appropriate body for regulating the rates of wages in any trade or industry other than the Civil Engineering Construction Industry to which Contractors undertaking works of civil engineering construction give effect by agreement or in practice or by reason of any Statute or Statutory Instrument there shall during the currency of the Contract be any increase or decrease in the wages or the rates of wages or in the allowances or rates of allowances (including allowances in respect of holidays) payable to or in respect of labour of any kind prevailing at the date of outbreak of war as then fixed by the said Board or such other body as aforesaid or by Statute or Statutory Instrument or any increase in the amount payable by the Contractor by virtue or in respect of any Scheme of State Insurance or if there shall be any increase or decrease in the cost prevailing at the date of the said outbreak of war of any materials consumable stores fuel or power

(e) Damage or injury caused by the explosion whenever occurring of any mine bomb shell grenade or other projectile missile or munition of war and whether occurring before or after the cessation of hostilities shall be deemed to be the consequence of any of the events mentioned in sub-clause (6)(a) of this Clause.

## SETTLEMENT OF DISPUTES

**Settlement of Disputes— Arbitration.**

**66.** (1) If a dispute or difference of any kind whatsoever shall arise between the Employer and the Contractor in connection with or arising out of the Contract or the carrying out of the Works including any dispute as to any decision opinion instruction direction certificate or valuation of the Engineer (whether during the progress of the Works or after their completion and whether before or after the determination abandonment or breach of the Contract) it shall be referred in writing to and be settled by the Engineer who shall state his decision in writing and give notice of the same to the Employer and the Contractor.

(and whether for permanent or temporary works) which increase or increases decrease or decreases shall result in an increase or decrease of cost to the Contractor in carrying out the Works the net increase or decrease of cost shall form an addition or deduction as the case may be to or from the Contract Price and be paid to or allowed by the Contractor accordingly.

(d)   If the cost of the Works to the Contractor shall be increased or decreased by reason of the provisions of any Statute or Statutory Instrument or other Government or Local Government Order or Regulation becoming applicable to the Works after the date of the said outbreak of war or by reason of any trade or industrial agreement entered in to after such date to which the Civil Engineering Construction Conciliation Board or any other body as aforesaid is party or gives effect or by reason of any amendment of whatsoever nature of the Working Rule Agreement of the said Board or of any other body as aforesaid or by reason of any other circumstance or thing attributable to or consequent on such outbreak of war such increase or decrease of cost as certified by the Engineer shall be reimbursed by the Employer to the Contractor or allowed by the Contractor as the case may be.

(e)   Damage or injury caused by the explosion whenever occuring of any mine bomb shell grenade or other projectile missile or munition of war and whether occurring before or after the cessation of hositilities shall be deemed to be the consequence of any of the events mentioned in sub-clause (6)(a) of this Clause.

## SETTLEMENT OF DISPUTES

*Previous Clause 66 concerning Arbitration has been rewritten to include the Institution of Civil Engineers' Conciliation Procedure.*

**Settlement of disputes**

**66**   (1)   Except as otherwise provided in these Conditions if a dispute of any kind whatsoever arises between the Employer and the Contractor in connection with or arising out of the Contract or the carrying out of the Works including any dispute as to any decision opinion instruction direction certificate or valuation of the Engineer (whether during the progress of the Works or after their completion and whether before or after the determination abandonment or breach of the Contract) it shall be settled in accordance with the following provisions.

*Substantially as previous Clause 66(1) lines 1-5.*

**Notice of Dispute**

(2)   For the purpose of sub-clauses (2) to (6) inclusive of this Clause a dispute shall be deemed to arise when one party serves on the Engineer a notice in writing (hereinafter called the Notice of Dispute) stating the nature of the dispute. Provided that no Notice of Dispute may be served unless the party wishing to do so has first taken any steps or invoked any procedure available elsewhere in the Contract in connection with the subject matter of such dispute and the other party or the Engineer as the case may be has

(a)   taken such step as may be required or

(b)   been allowed a reasonable time to take any such action.

*New Clause requiring the service of a Notice of Dispute.*

**Engineer's
Decision—Effect
on Contractor and
Employer.**

(2)   Unless the Contract shall have already been determined or abandoned the Contractor shall in every case continue to proceed with the Works with all due diligence and the Contractor and Employer shall both give effect forthwith to every such decision of the Engineer unless and until the same shall be revised by an arbitrator as hereinafter provided. Such decisions shall be final and binding upon the Contractor and the Employer unless and until the dispute or difference has been referred to arbitration as hereinafter provided and an award made and published.

**Arbitration—Time
for Engineer's
decision.**

(3) (a)   Where a Certificate of Completion of the whole of the Works has not been issued and
  (i) either the Employer or the Contractor be dissatisfied with any such decision of the Engineer
    or
  (ii) the Engineer shall fail to give such decision for a period of one calendar month after such referral in writing

then either the Employer or the Contractor may within 3 calendar months after receiving notice of such decision or within 3 calendar months after the expiration of the said period of one month (as the case may be) refer the dispute or difference to the arbitration of a person to be agreed upon by the parties by giving notice to the other party.

(b)   where a Certificate of Completion of the whole of the Works has been issued and
  (i) either the Employer or the Contractor be dissatisfied with any such decision of the Engineer
    or
  (ii) the Engineer shall fail to give such decision for a period of 3 calendar months after such referral in writing

then either the Employer or the Contractor may within 3 calendar months after receiving notice of such decision or within 3 calendar months after the expiration of the said period of 3 months (as the case may be) refer the dispute or difference to the arbitration of a person to be agreed upon by the parties by giving notice to the other party.

**Engineer's decision**

(3)   Every dispute notified under sub-clause (2) of this Clause shall be settled by the Engineer who shall state his decision in writing and give notice of the same to the Employer and the Contractor within the time limits set out in sub-clause (6) of this Clause.

*Substantially as previous Clause 66(1) lines 6 and 7.*

**Effect on Contractor and Employer**

(4)   Unless the Contract has already been determined or abandoned the Contractor shall in every case continue to proceed with the Works with all due diligence and the Contractor and the Employer shall both give effect forthwith to every such decision of the Engineer. Such decisions shall be final and binding upon the Contractor and the Employer unless and until as hereinafter provided either

(a)   the recommendation of a conciliator has been accepted by both parties or

(b)   the decision of the Engineer is revised by an arbitrator and an award made and published.

*Substantially as previous Clause 66(2) but now including reference to the acceptance of the recommendation of a conciliator.*

**Conciliation**

(5)   In relation to any dispute notified under sub-clause (2) of this Clause and in respect of which

(a)   the Engineer has given his decision or

(b)   the time for giving an Engineer's decision as set out in sub-clause (3) of this Clause has expired

and no Notice to Refer under sub-clause (6) of this Clause has been served either party may give notice in writing requiring the dispute to be considered under the Institution of Civil Engineers' Conciliation Procedure (1988) or any amendment or modification thereof being in force at the date of such notice and the dispute shall thereafter be referred and considered in accordance with the said Procedure. The recommendation of the conciliator shall be deemed to have been accepted in settlement of the dispute unless a written Notice to Refer under sub-clause(6) of this Clause is served within one calendar month of its receipt.

*New Clause providing for the use of the Institution of Civil Engineers' Conciliation Procedure. By use of a Notice to Refer either party has the right for the dispute to be referred to Arbitration instead of Conciliation. If no Notice to Refer is served by the due date following receipt of the conciliator's recommendation the recommendation is deemed to have been accepted.*

**Arbitration**

(6)   (a)   Where a Certificate of Substantial Completion of the whole of the Works has not been issued and either

(i)   the Employer or the Contractor is dissatisfied with any decision of the Engineer given under sub-clause (3) of this Clause or

(ii)   the Engineer fails to give such decision for a period of one calendar month after the service of the Notice of Dispute or

(iii)   the Employer or the Contractor is dissatisfied with any recommendation of a conciliator appointed under sub-clause (5) of this Clause

**President or Vice-President to act.**

(4) (a)   If the parties fail to appoint an arbitrator within one calendar month of either party serving on the other party a written Notice to Concur in the appointment of an arbitrator the dispute or difference shall be referred to a person to be appointed on the application of either party by the President for the time being of the Institution of Civil Engineers.

(b)   If an arbitrator declines the appointment or after appointment is removed by order of a competent court or is incapable of acting or dies and the parties do not within one calendar month of the vacancy arising fill the vacancy then either party may apply to the President for the time being of the Institution of Civil Engineers to appoint another arbitrator to fill the vacancy.

(c)   In any case where the President for the time being of the Institution of Civil Engineers is not able to exercise the functions conferred on him by this Clause the said functions may be exercised on his behalf by a Vice-President for the time being of the said Institution.

**ICE Arbitration Procedure (1983).**

(5) (a)   Any reference to arbitration shall be conducted in accordance with the Institution of Civil Engineers' Arbitration Procedure (1983) or any amendment or modification thereof being in force at the time of the appointment of the arbitrator. Such arbitrator shall have full power to open up review and revise any decision opinion instruction direction certificate or valuation of the Engineer and neither party shall be limited in the proceedings before such arbitrator to the evidence or arguments put before the Engineer for the purpose of obtaining his decision above referred to.

(b)   Any such reference to arbitration shall be deemed to be a submission to arbitration within the meaning of the Arbitration Act 1950 or any statutory re-enactment or amendment thereof for the time being in force. The award of the arbitrator shall be binding on all parties.

(c)   Any reference to arbitration may unless the parties otherwise agree in writing proceed notwithstanding that the Works are not then complete or alleged to be complete.

**Engineer as witness.**

(6)   No decision given by the Engineer in accordance with the foregoing provisions shall disqualify him from being called as a witness and giving evidence before the arbitrator on any matter whatsoever relevant to the dispute or difference so referred to the arbitrator as aforesaid.

then either the Employer or the Contractor may within 3 calendar months after receiving notice of such decision or within 3 calendar months after the expiry of the said period of one month or within one calendar month of receipt of the conciliator's recommendation (as the case may be) refer the dispute to the arbitration of a person to be agreed upon by the parties by serving on the other party a written Notice to Refer.

(b)  Where a Certificate of Substantial Completion of the whole of the Works has been issued the foregoing provisions shall apply save that the said periods of one calendar month referred to in (a) above shall be read as 3 calendar months.

*Substantially as previous Clause 66(3) but with provision also made for Arbitration if a conciliator's recommendation is not accepted.*

**President or Vice-President to act**

(7)  (a)  If the parties fail to appoint an arbitrator within one calendar month of either party serving on the other party written Notice to Concur in the appointment of an arbitrator the dispute or difference shall be referred to a person to be appointed on the application of either party by the President for the time being of the Institution of Civil Engineers.

(b)  If an arbitrator declines the appointment or after appointment is removed by order of a competent court or is incapable of acting or dies and the parties do not within one calendar month of the vacancy arising fill the vacancy then either party may apply to the President for the time being of the Institution of Civil Engineers to appoint another arbitrator to fill the vacancy.

(c)  In any case where the President for the time being of the Institution of Civil Engineers is not able to exercise the functions conferred on him by this Clause the said functions shall be exercised on his behalf by a Vice-President for the time being of the said Institution.

**Arbitration— procedure and powers**

(8)  (a)  Any reference to arbitration under this Clause shall be deemed to be a submission to arbitration within the meaning of the Arbitration Acts 1950 to 1979 or any statutory re-enactment or amendment thereof for the time being in force. The reference shall be conducted in accordance with the Institution of Civil Engineers Arbitration Procedure (1983) or any amendment or modification thereof being in force at the time of the appointment of the arbitrator. Such arbitrator shall have full power to open up review and revise any decision opinion instruction direction certificate or valuation of the Engineer.

(b)  Neither party shall be limited in the proceedings before such arbitrator to the evidence or arguments put before the Engineer for the purpose of obtaining his decision under sub-clause (3) of this Clause.

(c)  The award of the arbitrator shall be binding on all parties.

(d)  Unless the parties otherwise agree in writing any reference to arbitration may proceed notwithstanding that the Works are not then complete or alleged to be complete.

*Substantially as previous Clause 66(5).*

**Engineer as witness**

(9)  No decision given by the Engineer in accordance with the foregoing provisions shall disqualify him from being called as witness and giving evidence before the arbitrator on any matter whatsoever relevant to the dispute or difference so referred to the arbitrator.

**Application to Scotland.**

**67.** (1) If the Works are situated in Scotland the Contract shall in all respects be construed and operate as a Scottish contract and shall be interpreted in accordance with Scots Law and the provisions of this Clause shall apply.

(2) In the application of Clause 66 the word 'arbiter' shall be substituted for the word 'arbitrator'. Any reference to the Arbitration Act 1950 shall be deleted and for any reference to the Institution of Civil Engineers' Arbitration Procedure (1983) there shall be substituted a reference to the Institution of Civil Engineers' Arbitration Procedure (Scotland) (1983).

## NOTICES

**Service of Notice on Contractor.**

**68.** (1) Any notice to be given to the Contractor under the terms of the Contract shall be served by sending the same by post to or leaving the same at the Contractor's principal place of business (or in the event of the Contractor being a Company to or at its registered office).

**Service of Notice on Employer.**

(2) Any notice to be given to the Employer under the terms of the Contract shall be served by sending the same by post to or leaving the same at the Employer's last known address (or in the event of the Employer being a Company to or at its registered office).

## TAX MATTERS

**Tax Fluctuations.**

**69.** (1) The rates and prices contained in the Bill of Quantities take account of the levels and incidence at the date for return of tenders (hereinafter called " the relevant date") of the taxes levies and contributions (including national insurance contributions but excluding income tax and any levy payable under the Industrial Training Act 1964) which are by law payable by the Contractor in respect of his workpeople and the premiums and refunds (if any) which are by law payable to the Contractor in respect of his workpeople. Any such matter is hereinafter called " a labour-tax matter ".

The rates and prices contained in the Bill of Quantities do not take account of any level or incidence of the aforesaid matters where at the relevant date such level or incidence does not then have effect but although then known is to take effect at some later date. The taking effect of any such level or incidence at the later date shall for the purposes of sub-clause (2) of this Clause be treated as the occurrence of an event.

## APPLICATION TO SCOTLAND

**Application to Scotland**  **67**  (1)  If the Works are situated in Scotland the Contract shall in all respects be construed and operate as a Scottish contract and shall be interpreted in accordance with Scots Law and the provisions of this Clause shall apply.

(2)  In the application of these Conditions and in particular Clause 66 thereof

    (a)  the word "arbiter" shall be substituted for the word "arbitrator"

    (b)  for any reference to the "Arbitration Acts" there shall be substituted reference to the "Arbitration (Scotland) Act 1894"

    (c)  for any reference to the Institution of Civil Engineers Arbitration Procedure (1983) there shall be substituted a reference to the Institution of Civil Engineers Arbitration Procedure (Scotland) (1983) and

    (d)  notwithstanding any of the other provisions of these Conditions nothing therein shall be construed as excluding or otherwise affecting the right of a party to arbitration to call in terms of Section 3 of the Administration of Justice (Scotland) Act 1972 for the arbiter to state a case.

## NOTICES

**Service of notices on Contractor**  **68**  (1)  Any notice to be given to the Contractor under the terms of the Contract shall be served in writing at the Contractor's principal place of business (or in the event of the Contractor being a Company to or at its registered office).

**Service of notices on Employer**  (2)  Any notice to be given to the Employer under the terms of the Contract shall be served in writing at the Employer's last known address (or in the event of the Employer being a Company to or at its registered office).

## TAX MATTERS

**Labour-tax fluctuations**  **69**  (1)  The rates and prices contained in the Bill of Quantities shall be deemed to take account of the levels and incidence at the date for return of tenders of the taxes levies contributions premiums or refunds (including national insurance contributions but excluding income tax and any levy payable under the Industrial Training Act 1964) which are by law payable by or to the Contractor and his sub-contractors in respect of their workpeople engaged on the Contract.

The rates and prices contained in the Bill of Quantities do not take account of any level or incidence of the aforesaid matters where at the date for return of tenders such level or incidence does not then have effect but although then known is to take effect at some later date.

(2)   If after the relevant date there shall occur any of the events specified in sub-clause (3) of this Clause and as a consequence thereof the cost to the Contractor of performing his obligations under the Contract shall be increased or decreased then subject to the provisions of sub-clause (4) of this Clause the net amount of such increase or decrease shall constitute an addition to or deduction from the sums otherwise payable to the Contractor under the Contract as the case may require.

(3)   The events referred to in the preceding sub-clause are as follows:—

   (a)   any change in the level of any labour-tax matter;
   (b)   any change in the incidence of any labour-tax matter including the imposition of any new such matter or the abolition of any previously existing such matter.

(4)   In this Clause workpeople means persons employed by the Contractor on manual labour whether skilled or unskilled but for the purpose of ascertaining what if any additions or deductions are to be paid or allowed under this Clause account shall not be taken of any labour-tax matter in relation to any workpeople of the Contractor unless at the relevant time their normal place of employment is the Site.

(5)   Subject to the provisions of the Contract as to the placing of sub-contracts with Nominated Sub-contractors the Contractor may incorporate in any sub-contract made for the purpose of performing his obligations under the Contract provisions which are *mutatis mutandis* the same as the provisions of this Clause and in such event additions or deductions to be made in accordance with any such sub-contract shall also be made under the Contract as if the increase or decrease of cost to the sub-contractor had been directly incurred by the Contractor.

(6)   As soon as practicable after the occurrence of any of the events specified in sub-clause (3) of this Clause the Contractor shall give the Engineer notice thereof.   The Contractor shall keep such contemporary records as are necessary for the purpose of ascertaining the amount of any addition or deduction to be made in accordance with this Clause and shall permit the Engineer to inspect such records.   The Contractor shall submit to the Engineer with his monthly statements full details of every addition or deduction to be made in accordance with this Clause.   All certificates for payment issued after submission of such details shall take due account of the additions or deductions to which such details relate.   Provided that the Engineer may if the Contractor fails to submit full details of any deduction nevertheless take account of such deduction when issuing any certificate for payment.

**Value Added Tax**

**70.**   (1)   In this Clause " exempt supply " " invoice " " tax " " taxable person " and " taxable supply " have the same meanings as in Part I of the Finance Act 1972 (hereinafter referred to as " the Act ") including any amendment or re-enactment thereof and any reference to the Value Added Tax (General) Regulations 1972 (S.I. 1972/1147) (hereinafter referred to as the V.A.T. Regulations) shall be treated as a reference to any enactment corresponding to those regulations for the time being in force in consequence of any amendment or re-enactment of those regulations.

(2)   The Contractor shall be deemed not to have allowed in his tender for the tax payable by him as a taxable person to the Commissioners of Customs and Excise being tax chargeable on any taxable supplies to the Employer which are to be made under the Contract.

(3)  (a)   The Contractor shall not in any statement submitted under Clause 60 include any element on account of tax in any item or claim contained in or submitted with the statement.

   (b)   The Contractor shall concurrently with the submission of the statement referred to in sub-clause (3)(a) of this Clause furnish the Employer with a written estimate showing those supplies of goods and services and the values thereof included in the said statement and on which tax will be chargeable under Regulation 21 of the V.A.T. Regulations at a rate other than zero.

(4)   At the same time as payment (other than payment in accordance with this sub-clause) for goods or services which were the subject of a taxable supply provided by the Contractor as a taxable person to the Employer is made in accordance with the Contract there shall also be paid by the Employer a sum (separately identified by the Employer and in this Clause referred to as " the tax payment ") equal to the amount of tax payable by the Contractor on that supply.   Within seven days of each payment the Contractor shall:—

   (a)   if he agrees with that tax payment or any part thereof issue to the Employer an authenticated receipt of the kind referred to in Regulation 21(2) of the V.A.T. Regulations in respect of that payment or that part; and

   (b)   if he disagrees with that tax payment or any part thereof notify the Employer in writing stating the grounds of his disagreement.

(2)    If after the date for return of tenders there shall occur any change in the level and/or incidence of any such taxes levies contributions premiums or refunds the Contractor shall so inform the Engineer and the net increase or decrease shall be taken into account in arriving at the Contract Price. The Contractor shall supply the information necessary to support any consequent adjustment to the Contract Price. All certificates for payment issued after submission of such information shall take due account of the additions or deductions to which such information relates.

*Clause 69 has been simplified.*

**Value Added Tax** **70**    (1)    The Contractor shall be deemed not to have allowed in his tender for the tax payable by him as a taxable person to the Commissioners of Customs and Excise being tax chargeable on any taxable supplies to the Employer which are to be made under the Contract.

**Engineer's certificates net of Value Added Tax**    (2)    All certificates issued by the Engineer under Clause 60 shall be net of Value Added Tax.

In addition to the payments due under such certificates the Employer shall separately identify and pay to the Contractor any Value Added Tax properly chargeable by the Commissioners of Customs and Excise on the supply to the Employer of any goods and/or services by the Contractor under the Contract.

**Disputes**    (3)    If any dispute difference or question arises between either the Employer or the Contractor and the Commissioners of Customs and Excise in relation to any tax chargeable or alleged to be chargeable in connection with the Contract or the Works each shall render to the other such support and assistance as may be necessary to resolve the dispute difference or question.

**Clause 66 not applicable**    (4)    Clause 66 shall not apply to any dispute difference or question arising under this Clause.

*Clause 70 has been simplified.*

(5) (a) If any dispute difference or question arises between the Employer and the Contractor in relation to any of the matters specified in Section 40(1) of the Act then:—

    (i) if the Employer so requires the Contractor shall refer the matter to the said Commissioners for their decision on it

    (ii) if the Contractor refers the matter to the said Commissioners (whether or not in pursuance of sub-paragraph (i) above) and the Employer is dissatisfied with their decision on the matter the Contractor shall at the Employer's request refer the matter to a Value Added Tax Tribunal by way of appeal under Section 40 of the Act whether the Contractor is so dissatisfied or not

    (iii) a sum of money equal to the amount of tax which the Contractor in making a deposit with the said Commissioners under Section 40(3)(a) of the Act is required so to deposit shall be paid to the Contractor; and

    (iv) if the Employer requires the Contractor to refer such a matter to the Tribunal in accordance with sub-paragraph (ii) above then he shall reimburse the Contractor any costs and any expenses reasonably and properly incurred in making that reference less any costs awarded to the Contractor by the Tribunal and the decision of the Tribunal shall be binding on the Employer to the same extent as it binds the Contractor.

    (b) Clause 66 shall not apply to any dispute difference or question arising under paragraph (a) of this sub-clause.

(6) (a) The Employer shall without prejudice to his rights under any other Clause hereof be entitled to recover from the Contractor:—

    (i) any tax payment made to the Contractor of a sum which is in excess of the sum (if any) which in all the circumstances was due in accordance with sub-clause (4) of this Clause

    (ii) in respect of any sum of money deposited by the Contractor pursuant to sub-clause (5)(a)(iii) of this Clause a sum equal to the amount repaid under Section 40(4) of the Act together with any interest thereon which may have been determined thereunder.

    (b) If the Contractor shall establish that the Commissioners have charged him in respect of a taxable supply for which he has received payment under this Clause tax greater in amount than the sum paid to him by the Employer the Employer shall subject to the provisions of sub-clause (5) of this Clause pay to the Contractor a sum equal to the difference between the tax previously paid and the tax charged to the Contractor by the Commissioners.

(7) If after the date for return of tenders the descriptions of any supplies of goods or services which at the date of tender are taxable or exempt supplies are with effect after the date for return of tenders modified or extended by or under the Act and that modification or extension shall result in the Contractor having to pay either more or less tax or greater or smaller amounts attributable to tax and that tax or those amounts as the case may be shall be a direct expense or direct saving to the Contractor in carrying out the Works and not recoverable or allowable under the Contract or otherwise then there shall be paid to or allowed by the Contractor as appropriate a sum equivalent to that tax or amounts as the case may be.

Provided always that before that tax is included in any payment by the Employer or those amounts are included in any certificate by the Engineer as the case may be the Contractor shall supply all the information the Engineer requires to satisfy himself as to the Contractor's entitlement under this sub-clause.

(8) The Contractor shall upon demand pay to the Employer the amount of any sum due in accordance with sub-clauses (6) and (7) of this Clause and it shall be deemed a debt due by the Contractor to the Employer and shall be recoverable accordingly.

## METRICATION

**Metrication.** **71.** (1) If any materials described in the Contract or ordered by the Engineer are described by dimensions in the metric or imperial measure and having used his best endeavours the Contractor cannot without undue delay or additional expense or at all procure such materials in the measure specified in the Contract but can obtain such materials in the other measure to dimensions approximating to those described in the Contract or ordered by the Engineer then the Contractor shall forthwith give written notice to the Engineer of these facts stating the dimensions to which such materials are procurable in the other measure. Such notice shall where practicable be given in sufficient time to enable the Engineer to consider and if necessary give effect to any design change which may be required and to avoid delay in the performance of the Contractor's other obligations under the Contract. Any additional cost or expense incurred by the Contractor as a result of any delay arising out of the Contractor's default under this sub-clause shall be borne by the Contractor.

*Previous Clause 71 omitted as not now required.*

(2)    As soon as practicable after the receipt of any such notice under the preceding sub-clause the Engineer shall if he is satisfied that the Contractor has used his best endeavours to obtain materials to the dimensions described in the Contract or ordered by the Engineer and that they are not obtainable without undue delay or without putting the Contractor to additional expense either:—

(a)    instruct the Contractor pursuant to Clause 13 to supply such materials (despite such delay or expense) in the dimensions described in the Contract or originally ordered by the Engineer; or

(b)    give an order to the Contractor pursuant to Clause 51:—

(i)    to supply such materials to the dimensions stated in his said notice to be procurable instead of to the dimensions described in the Contract or originally ordered by the Engineer; or

(ii)    to make some other variation whereby the need to supply such materials to the dimensions described in the Contract or originally ordered by the Engineer will be avoided.

(3)    This Clause shall apply irrespective of whether the materials in question are to be supplied in accordance with the Contract directly by the Contractor or indirectly by a Nominated Sub-contractor.

## SPECIAL CONDITIONS

**Special Conditions.**

72.    The following special conditions form part of the Conditions of Contract.

(Note: Any special conditions which it is desired to incorporate in the conditions of contract should be numbered consecutively with the foregoing conditions of contract.)

## SPECIAL CONDITIONS

**Special conditions**  **71**  The following special conditions form part of the Conditions of Contract.

(Note. Any special conditions including contract price fluctuation which it is desired to incorporate in the conditions of contract should be numbered consecutively with the foregoing conditions of contract).